ISBN: 0-9826608-5-5
ISBN 13: 978-0-982-6608-5-0

You can visit us online at: ***www.JacKrisPublishing.com***

Printed in the United States of America.

Ver. 1.0.0-1

Second Semester

Preface

We have designed this thorough program to be user friendly for both teacher and student. This program is arranged in **36 weekly lessons**. Lessons 19 through 36 are contained in this Second Semester book. Lessons 1-18 are contained in *Winning With Writing*, Level 4, First Semester book. Each lesson consists of five exercises labeled **Day 1** through **Day 5**.

Writing is very similar to other things in life; you need to have a plan and be well organized before you start. For example, you would never think of building a house without first having blueprints (plans) that clearly define the layout of the house. Without first having a plan, the house would certainly end up as a disconnected, unorganized mess.

In other words, you need to be organized before doing anything that is not obvious or simple. As I mentioned, being prepared before starting the actual drafting process is necessary. When writing we organize our writing by adhering to the following processes:

Outlining Process

1. The student first thinks of an idea (main topic) about which he wants to write.
2. The student then thinks of details that support his main topic. Instead of placing these details on a blank piece of paper, we provide a rough outline form when needed. This rough outline form is simply a place where general ideas are written in an organized manner. Completing the rough outline is the first step in organizing your writing.
3. After the student is through placing his ideas on the rough outline, it is used to build a final outline. It is during the transfer of information from the rough outline to the final outline that the details contained on the rough outline are further organized and developed into sentences for the actual writing assignment.

Drafting Process

1. The final outline is used as a guide to write a rough draft of the writing assignment. Typically, the student merely transfers the information contained on the final outline to the rough draft of the writing.
2. The student then edits the rough draft for grammar and content.
3. The final draft of the writing assignment is then written.

We believe this process is the easiest and most straight-forward way to write any type of writing. By using these processes, the difficult task of writing becomes extremely simple and easy for anyone. The processes taught in this book can be used for any type of writing of any length ranging from a single paragraph to an entire book.

Level 4 - Second Semester

Table of Contents

Student's Name: ______________________

Winning With Writing Level 4

Second Semester

Date: ____________________

A Story of Senses

A **descriptive writing** tells about a person, place, or thing. The goal of a good **descriptive writing** is to involve the reader in the story as much as possible. You want the reader to feel like they were actually there during the events of the story. One way to involve a reader in a story is to use **adjectives** that describe our senses. An adjective is a word that describes another word. As humans we have five senses: **touch**, **sight**, **hearing**, **taste**, and **smell**.

Here is a sample story that describes many types of senses to help the reader feel like they are a part of the story.

My Trip to the Supermarket

My name is Ethan, and I enjoy going to the supermarket with my Dad. We always make a grocery list on an old tablet that is covered with a rough leather surface. Dad usually lets me write the list because his writing looks more like scribbling.

As soon as we arrive at the store I can smell the aroma of fresh bread baking from the parking lot. The freshly paved parking lot is bustling with other shoppers. The outside of the store is colorful with huge banners displaying the weekly sales.

Once inside the huge store, there are many things to experience. Dad and I always like to spend a little time in the bakery area. There are many different types of bread that you can lightly squeeze to determine freshness. Also, the delicatessen has over a hundred different types of cheeses. Some feel really squishy and smell like rotten eggs. Dad said those are the best kind of cheeses. Often there is a platter sitting out with free samples of cheese. One time I tried a piece of the stinky cheese, and it not only smelled like an old shoe, but also it tasted like something rotten.

After we spend a little time in the delicatessen, we wander around the store to shop for the items on our list. Occasionally we will hear a cashier ask loudly for a price check over the scratchy intercom system. You can also hear the sounds of other people talking as they shop.

I always enjoy going to the store with Dad because there are so many things to touch, smell, hear, see, and feel.

A. What are the five senses a human possesses? Write an **X** next to each correct answer below.

1. ___ sight
2. ___ impending weather patterns
3. ___ hearing
4. ___ intuition
5. ___ touch
6. ___ vision
7. ___ smell

B. What is the goal of a good descriptive story?

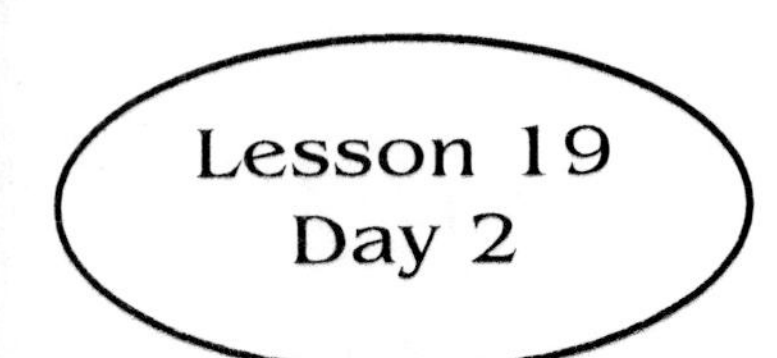

Date: ____________________

A Story of Senses

A. Looking back at the example story from Day 1, answer the following questions.

1. Who is the main character in this story?

____

____

2. How many different types of cheeses are there at the delicatessen? Circle the correct answer.

   a. about 10

   b. over a 100

   c. millions

   d. less than 100

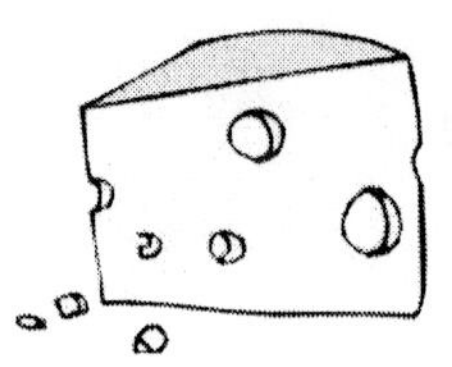

3. How does the main character test the bread to see if it's fresh? Circle the correct answer.

   a. He looks at the expiration date.

   b. He looks for mold on the bread.

   c. He squeezes it.

   d. He doesn't test the bread.

4. What kind of cheese does the main character's Dad like? Circle the correct answer.

   a. Swiss cheese

   b. stinky cheese

   c. yellow cheese

   d. whatever is being given away as a free sample

5. Does the main character like stinky cheese?

____

____

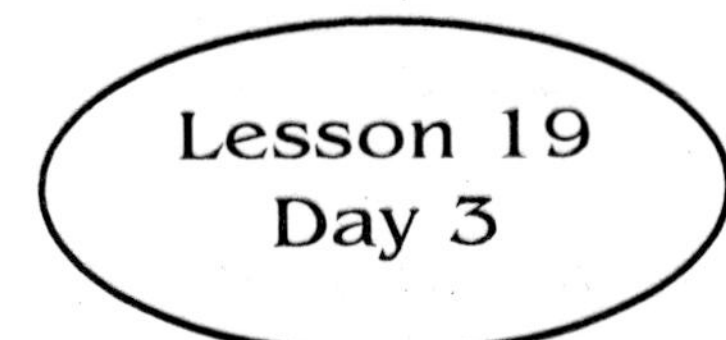

Date: ____________________

A Story of Senses

A. Once again look back at the sample story from Day 1. What kinds of things did Ethan sense? Answer the questions below for each sense.

1. sight

2. hearing

3. touch

4. smell

5. taste

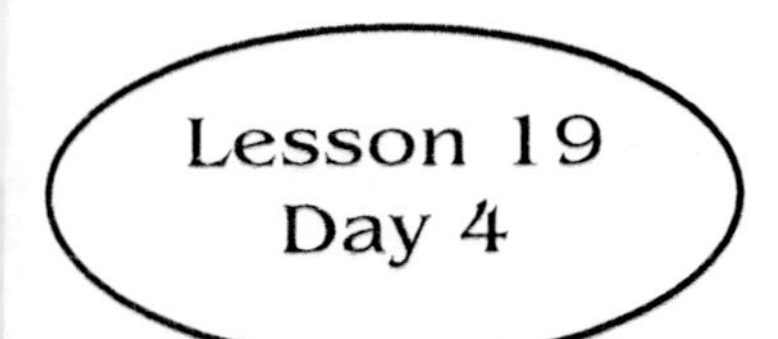

Date: ____________________

A Story of Senses

A. Answer each question below by circling the correct answer.

1. How are the following things sensed: loudness, a screech, music?
   a. sight
   b. hearing
   c. smell
   d. taste
2. How are the following things sensed: darkness, brightness, colors?
   a. sight
   b. hearing
   c. touch
   d. taste
3. How are the following things sensed: sweetness, bland, sour, saltiness?
   a. hearing
   b. touch
   c. smell
   d. taste
4. How are the following things sensed: stink, aroma, perfume?
   a. sight
   b. hearing
   c. touch
   d. smell
5. How are the following things sensed: sharpness, roughness, softness?
   a. sight
   b. hearing
   c. touch
   d. smell

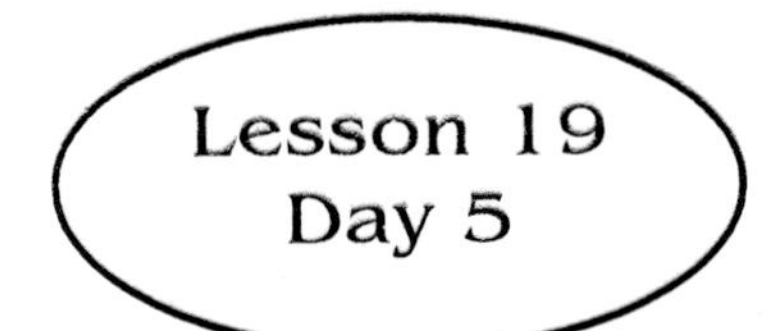

Date: ______________________

A Story of Senses

A. Write a short paragraph that contains several **sense adjectives**. You can write about **a parade you've seen**, **a day at the beach**, or you can **come up with your own story**. You do not have to outline for this paragraph.

Date: ____________________

Using Adjectives and Adverbs to Describe

Of course we know that verbs can be used to make sentences more interesting, but we can also use **adverbs** to make our sentences more interesting. An **adverb** often describes a **verb** in a sentence. An **adverb** makes a sentence more interesting by telling **how**, **when**, or **where** something happens.

Adverbs that tell **how** something happens usually end in the letters **-ly**. The following sentence contains an adverb that tells **how**.

The wind blew **softly**.

Notice that the word **blew** actually tells **what** is happening. It is a **verb**. The adverb **softly** tells **how** the wind **blew**.

An **adverb** can also tell **when** or **where** something happens.

The wind blew **earlier**.

The wind blew **outside**.

The words **earlier** and **outside** tell **when** and **where** the wind **blew**.

A. Below are sentences that have **adverbs** that tell **how**, **when**, or **where**. Underline the **adverb** in each sentence.

1. The sun shone brightly.
2. Tom quickly wrote a note.
3. Terri always skips.
4. The cat slept there.
5. I almost stumbled.
6. The vase suddenly fell.
7. I stood yesterday.
8. He spoke today.
9. I sang hesitantly.
10. The ball suddenly popped.

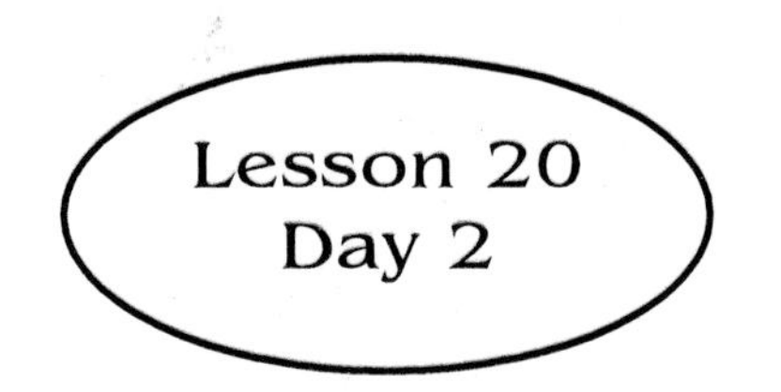

Date: ____________________

Using Adjectives and Adverbs to Describe

To make sentences more interesting we can use **adjectives** to describe **nouns**. An **adjective** tells **which one**, **what kind**, or **how many** about a **noun**.

Dad changed the tire.

This sentence simply makes the statement that **Dad changed the tire**.

Dad changed the flat tire.

In this sentence, the adjective **flat** describes the tire. An **adjective** usually comes right before the noun it describes.

A. Underline the **adjectives** in each sentence.

1. Jane has a pretty car.
2. Dad drove the old bus.
3. He sold the red house.
4. Gabe baked soft cookies.
5. He cut the long grass.
6. I flew in the large airplane.
7. Kate sent a short letter to Mike.
8. The squeaky door scared me.
9. The green trees swayed.
10. Ed bought plump grapes.
11. Tom uses red onions.
12. A small ball rolled.
13. The cold water froze.
14. I used the new computer.

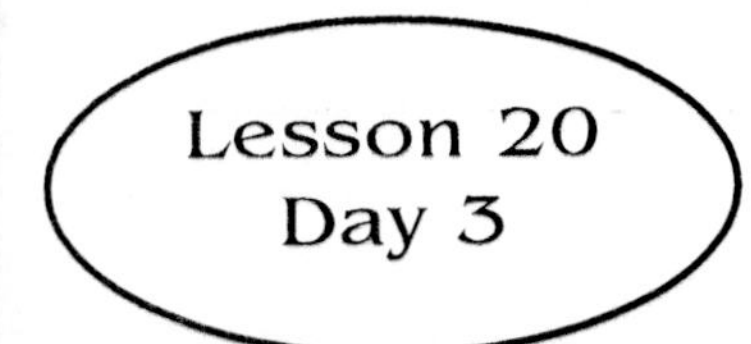

Date: ______________________

Using Adjectives and Adverbs to Describe

A. Underline the **adverb** in each sentence and circle the **adjective**.

1. The blue truck backfired loudly.
2. The tall girl ran yesterday.
3. The hot food sat there.
4. The young boy spoke slowly.
5. Debra skillfully sculpted the wet clay.
6. The talented artist painted quietly.
7. The short athlete jumped high.
8. We washed the old dog earlier.
9. The patient woman stood still.
10. We always bake fresh bread.

B. Replace the **adjectives** you circled with your own **adjectives** for each sentence.

1. ______________________

2. ______________________

3. ______________________

4. ______________________

5. ______________________

6. ______________________

7. ______________________

8. ______________________

9. ______________________

10. ______________________

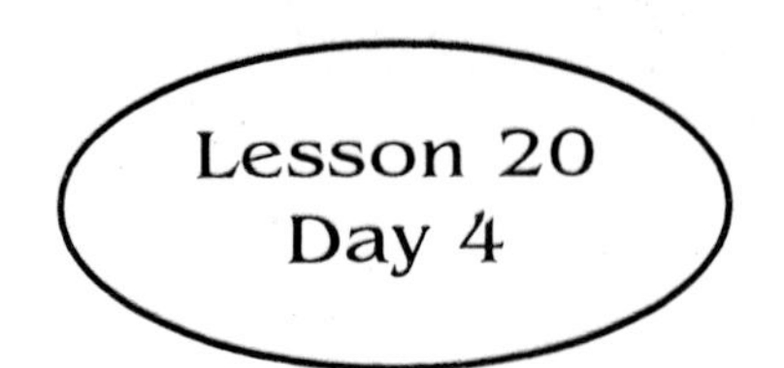

Date: ______________________

Using Adjectives and Adverbs to Describe

Sometimes we use **more than one adjective** to describe a noun.

A. Once you have completed this exercise, the sentences below will each contain more than one **adjective** that describe the same **noun**. Write another **adjective** on the lines provided to complete each sentence.

1. The ______________ red truck crept away.
2. We looked for ______________ new tires for our car.
3. Theresa bought a large______________ rug.
4. The ______________ angry man yelled.
5. Randy wore a ______________ and yellow shirt.
6. Gail swam in the ______________ and deep water.
7. The______________ loud boys were playing over there.
8. Jean has long ______________ hair.
9. Stan walked down the dark and______________ street.
10. Sharks have______________ jagged teeth.

Date: ____________________

Using Adjectives and Adverbs to Describe

A. Use your own **adverbs** or **adjectives** to complete each sentence below. Some sentences need an adverb, and some need an adjective.

1. Bob ____________________ studied the map.
2. The ____________________ apple was his.
3. Henry ate his meal ____________________.
4. She played the ____________________ horn.
5. I met Adam ____________________ at the fair.
6. Leslie drove the ____________________ car.
7. I chose the ____________________ flower.
8. It was a ____________________ ride.
9. Alan overslept ____________________.
10. Dad fell from the ____________________ ladder.
11. Daniel found the ____________________ remote control.
12. Mary washed her hands ____________________.

Lesson 21
Day 1

Date: ____________________

Comparisons

Adjectives are often used to **compare** nouns or pronouns. Usually, when comparing **two** things, the ending **-er** is added to most adjectives that have **one** or **two syllables**.

My mother is **slower** than Ben.

When comparing three or more things, the ending **-est** is used with adjectives that have **one syllable** and some that have **two syllables**.

My mother is the **slowest** person of all.

One Thing	Comparing Two Things	Comparing Three Things
mean	meaner	meanest
high	higher	highest
pretty	prettier	prettiest

A. Circle the correct word to complete each sentence.

1. Matthew is (taller, tallest) than my brother.
2. That is the (larger, largest) rock I have ever seen.
3. She has the (prettier, prettiest) garden in our neighborhood.
4. Your house is (bigger, biggest) than ours.
5. Kendall is the (smarter, smartest) boy I know.
6. That dog is (shorter, shortest) than that cat.
7. This has been the (wetter, wettest) day of the year.

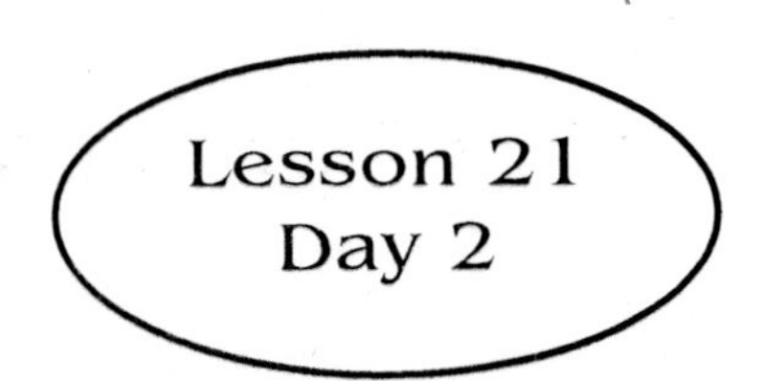

Date: ____________________

Comparisons

More, **most**, **less**, and **least** are often used to compare adjectives that have **three or more syllables**, and also some **two-syllable adjectives**.

This puzzle is **more difficult** than that one.

Today is **less humid** than yesterday.

This puzzle is the **most difficult** of all.

Today is the **least humid** day of the week.

One Thing	Comparing Two Things	Comparing Three Things
powerful	more powerful	most powerful
reliable	more reliable	most reliable
difficult	less difficult	least difficult

A. Write an **X** next to each group of comparing words that are written correctly.

1.____ enjoyable, more enjoyable, most enjoyable

2.____ painful, less painful, least painful

3.____ neat, more neat, most neatest

4.____ comfortable, more comfortable, most comfortable

5.____ more smart, most smart, smarter

6.____ expensive, more expensive, most expensive

7.____ harder, hardest, most hardest

Date: ____________________

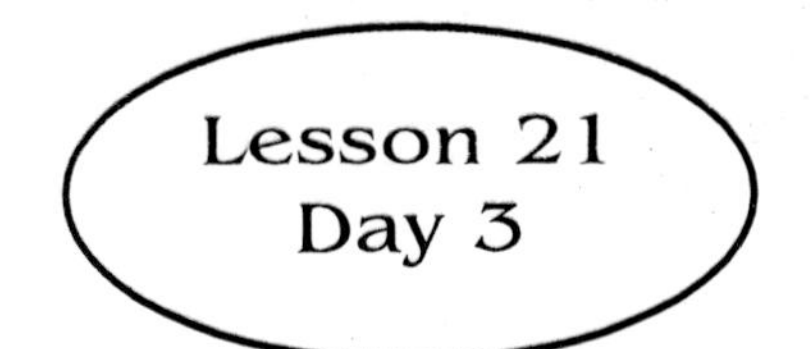

Comparisons

A. Underline the words that compare in the paragraph below. Write the words you underlined on the lines below.

My smaller sister and I were hungry and wanted a piece of the cake Mom made yesterday. Mom put the cake on the largest platter we had because it was bigger than any cake she had ever made. The cake was also placed on the tallest counter in the house to keep our dog away. Since I am taller than my tiniest sister, I reached the cake. I quickly cut two pieces of the cake. Mine was a larger than hers. This was the tastiest cake I had ever eaten. I think the cake was more enjoyable for me than it was her because I was looking forward to that cake longer than she was!

1. ____________________ 6. ____________________

2. ____________________ 7. ____________________

3. ____________________ 8. ____________________

4. ____________________ 9. ____________________

5. ____________________ 10. ____________________

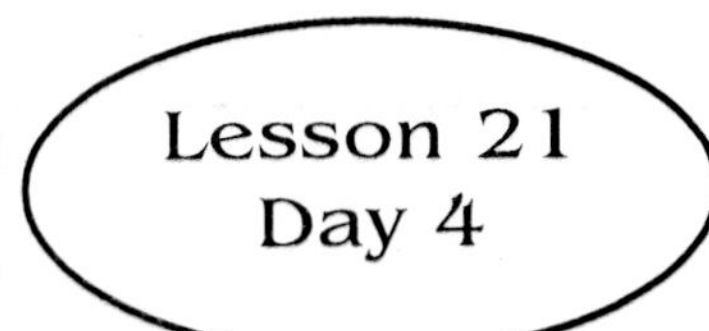

Date: ______________________

Comparisons

A. Write an **X** on the line of each sentence that uses comparing words correctly.

1.____ This chair is heavier than that one.

2.____ This paint dried fastest than the other paint.

3.____ Brandon is taller than Bradley.

4.____ We stayed longest than he did.

5.____ This painting is more beautiful than that one.

6.____ Our last vacation was the most enjoyable of all.

7.____ Did Billy buy the most expensive watch?

8.____ These old shoes are dirtiest than those shoes.

9.____ Barry was more stingiest than his brother.

10.____ David was stingier than Barry.

11.____ The red couch was more comfortabler than the blue one.

12.____ That chair is the most comfortable one in the whole house.

13.____ The fire on the stove is hotter than the campfire.

14.____ That box is most heavy than the rest.

15.____ It rained harder today than it did yesterday.

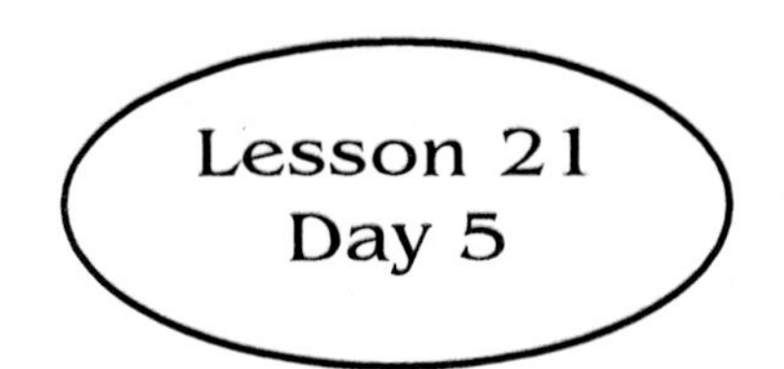

Date: ______________________

Comparison

A. Write your own paragraph. You can write about **choosing a toy to purchase for a friend**, **your favorite kind of dog**, or **a main topic of your own**. Use comparison adjectives in your paragraph.

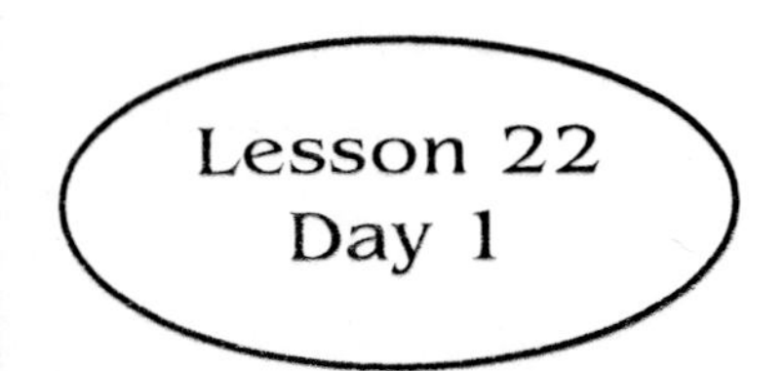

Date: ____________________

Descriptive Writing

Descriptive writing tells about a person, place, or thing. The goal of a good **descriptive writing** is to involve the reader in the story as much as possible. You want the reader to feel like they were actually there during the events of the story. In this lesson you will write a **three** paragraph descriptive writing that includes one introductory paragraph, one subtopic paragraph (body), and one concluding paragraph.

One way to involve a reader in a story is to use adjectives that describe our senses.

Think of a **main topic** for a story that you can describe by using the **five senses**. You can tell a descriptive story about **getting snowed in**, **going to the baseball park**, or come up with a **main topic of your own**. Before you settle on a main topic, answer the following questions to yourself:

1. Is your main topic something interesting that people will want to read?
2. Who is your audience?
3. Is your main topic too broad?
4. Is your main topic too narrow?

We will now start the writing process for **descriptive writing**.

Outlining Process
A. Complete the rough outline
B. Complete the final outline

Drafting Process
A. Complete the rough draft
B. Edit the rough draft
C. Complete the final draft

A. Complete the rough outline for your descriptive writing assignment.

Outlining Process

We will now begin your descriptive writing assignment with the outlining process. Outlining is the process where information about the writing is gathered in order to complete a rough outline and a final outline.

The entire outlining process is explained in **Appendix B**. Since this is the first time you are developing a writing with more than one paragraph, you should turn to Appendix B and familiarize yourself with the outlining process for multiple paragraphs. The outlining process for multiple paragraphs really isn't that much different than the outlining process for single paragraphs. However, there are **some** differences that you need to know.

Whether or not you use Appendix B, you still need to complete the rough outline and the final outline in this lesson.

Complete the rough outline

Rough Outline

Main Topic:

Subtopic #1:

Details:

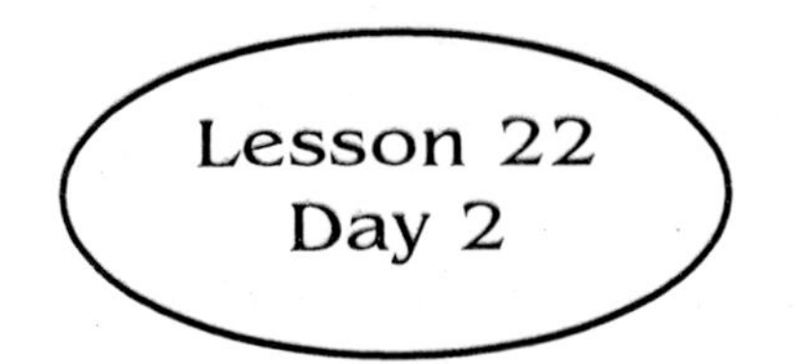

Date: ______________________

Descriptive Writing

Complete the final outline

Final Outline

Introductory Paragraph:

Subtopic #1:

Topic Sentence:

Detail Sentences:

Ending Sentence: (written after the topic sentence and detail sentences)

Concluding Paragraph:

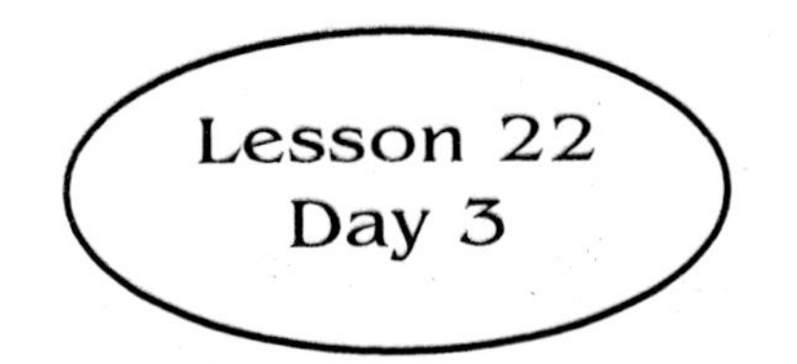

Date: ____________________

Descriptive Writing

Drafting Process

<u>Complete the rough draft</u>

So far you have spent quite a bit of time filling out the rough outline and the final outline. As a result, your final outline has all of the necessary pieces to complete your writing.

If you think of something you want to add while you are writing your rough draft, please do so. The final outline will now be used as a guide to write a rough draft.

Start by writing your **introductory paragraph**, sentences for each **subtopic** (topic sentence, detail sentences, and ending sentence), and **concluding paragraph** on the lines below.

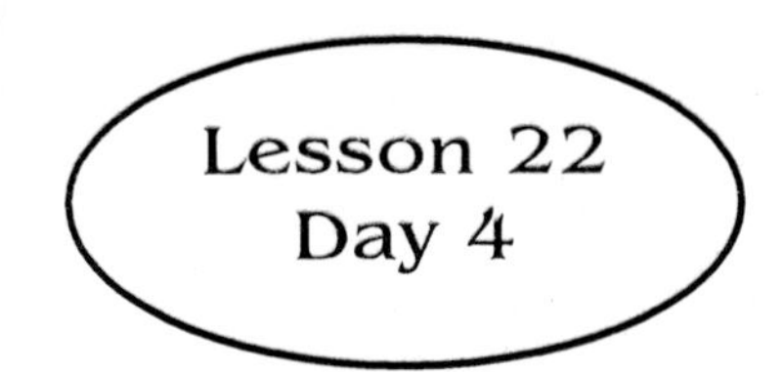

Date: ____________________

Descriptive Writing

Edit the rough draft

It is now time to **edit** the rough draft you wrote on Day 3. Use the editing marks shown in **Appendix C** to correct any mistakes.

Do your paragraphs say what you want them to say? Do the words you chose make sense?

Look for and fix the following errors: 1) incorrectly used, misspelled, or misplaced words, 2) incorrect or missing spacing, 3) incorrect, missing, or misplaced punctuation, and 4) incorrect or missing capitalization.

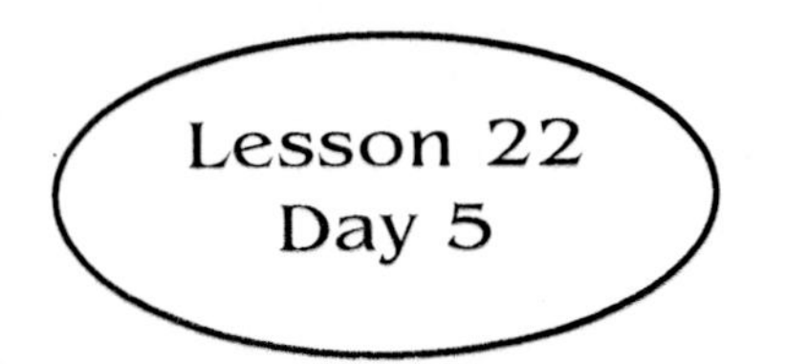

Date: ____________________

Descriptive Writing

Complete the final draft

On Day 4 you edited your paragraphs. Today you will rewrite your paragraphs in their final draft form.

Read your paragraphs one more time. Do your sentences flow well from one to the other? Does your entire story make sense? Can you make it even better by adding 1) **time order words**, 2) **strong verbs**, 3) **adverbs**, 4) **exact nouns**, or 5) **descriptive adjectives**? Rewrite your edited paragraphs below.

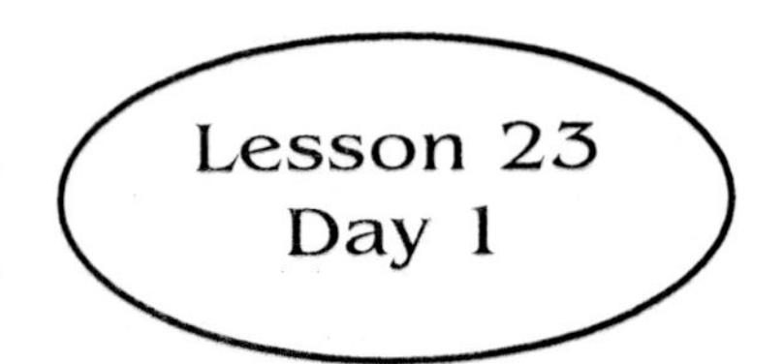

Date: ______________________

Descriptive Writing

In this lesson you will write a **three** paragraph **descriptive writing**. Think of another main topic for a story that you can describe by using the **five senses**. You could write about **your favorite dessert**, **something that quenches your thirst**, or come up with **your own main topic**.

We will now start the writing process for a **descriptive writing**.

Outlining Process
A. Complete the rough outline
B. Complete the final outline

Drafting Process
A. Complete the rough draft
B. Edit the rough draft
C. Complete the final draft

Outlining Process

We will now begin writing your descriptive writing assignment with the outlining process. Outlining is the process where information about the writing is gathered in order to complete a rough outline and a final outline.

The entire outlining process is explained in **Appendix B**. If you need help in completing the rough outline or the final outline, use Appendix B. Whether or not you use Appendix B, you still need to complete the rough outline and the final outline in this lesson.

Complete the rough outline

Rough Outline

Main Topic:

Subtopic #1:

Details:

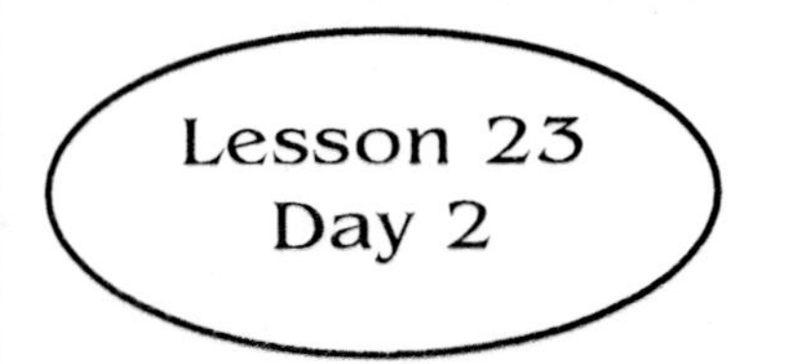

Date: ____________________

Descriptive Writing

Complete the final outline

Final Outline

Introductory Paragraph:

Subtopic 1#:

Topic Sentence:

Detail Sentences:

Ending Sentence: (written after the topic sentence and detail sentences)

Concluding Paragraph:

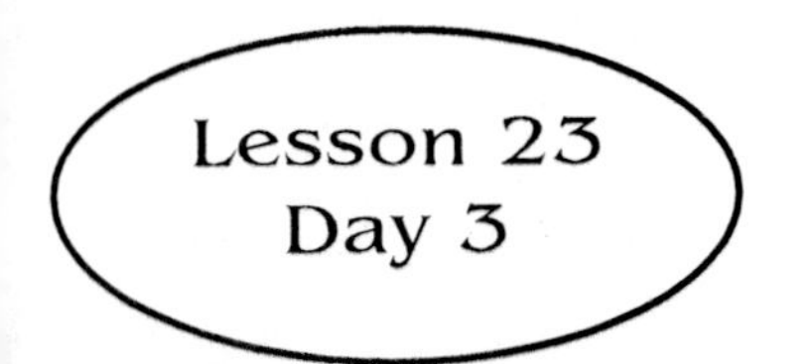

Date: ______________________

Descriptive Writing

Complete the rough draft

So far you have spent quite a bit of time filling out the rough outline and the final outline. As a result, your final outline has all of the necessary pieces to complete your writing.

If you think of something you want to add while you are writing your rough draft, please do so. The final outline will now be used as a guide to write a rough draft.

Start by writing your **introductory paragraph**, sentences for each **subtopic** (topic sentence, detail sentences, and ending sentence), and **concluding paragraph** on the lines below.

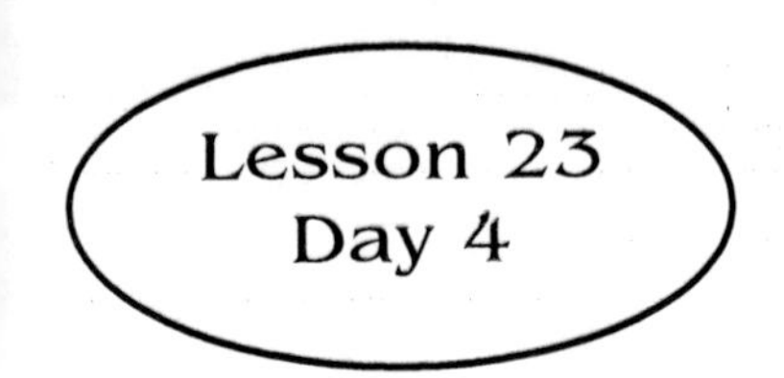

Date: ______________________

Descriptive Writing

Edit the rough draft

It is now time to **edit** the rough draft you wrote on Day 3. Use the editing marks shown in **Appendix C** to correct any mistakes.

Do your paragraphs say what you want them to say? Do the words you chose make sense?

Look for and fix the following errors: 1) incorrectly used, misspelled, or misplaced words, 2) incorrect or missing spacing, 3) incorrect, missing, or misplaced punctuation, and 4) incorrect or missing capitalization.

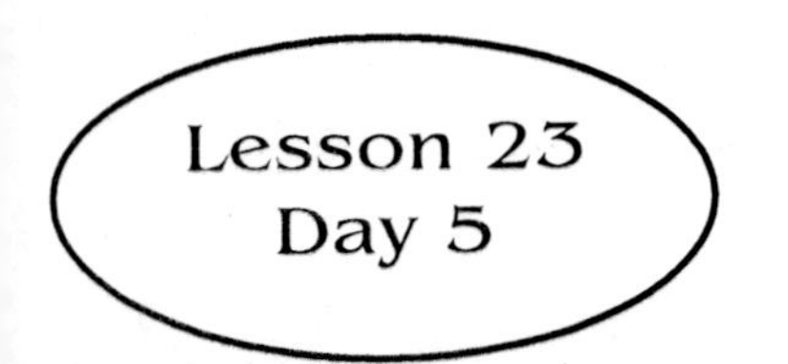

Date: ____________________

Descriptive Writing

Complete the final draft

On Day 4 you edited your paragraphs. Today you will rewrite your paragraphs in their final draft form.

Read your paragraphs one more time. Do your sentences flow well from one to the other? Does your entire story make sense? Can you make it even better by adding 1) **time order words**, 2) **strong verbs**, 3) **adverbs**, 4) **exact nouns**, or 5) **descriptive adjectives**? Rewrite your edited paragraphs below.

Date: ____________________

Review of a Story of Senses

A. Answer each question below by circling the correct answer.

1. How are the following things sensed: a voice, a bark, a horn?
   a. sight
   b. hearing
   c. smell
   d. taste

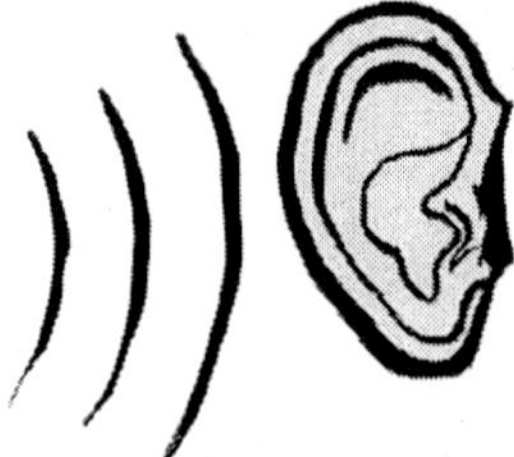

2. How are the following things sensed: a picture, a sunset, a smile?
   a. sight
   b. hearing
   c. touch
   d. taste

3. How are the following things sensed: tart, sweet, spicy?
   a. hearing
   b. touch
   c. sight
   d. taste

4. How are the following things sensed: garbage, dirty diapers, burnt food?
   a. sight
   b. hearing
   c. touch
   d. smell

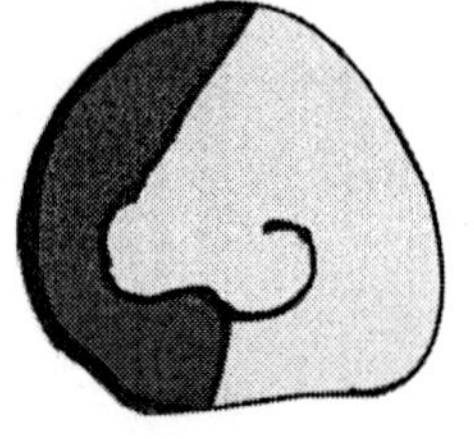

5. How are the following things sensed: wet, slippery, hard?
   a. sight
   b. hearing
   c. touch
   d. smell

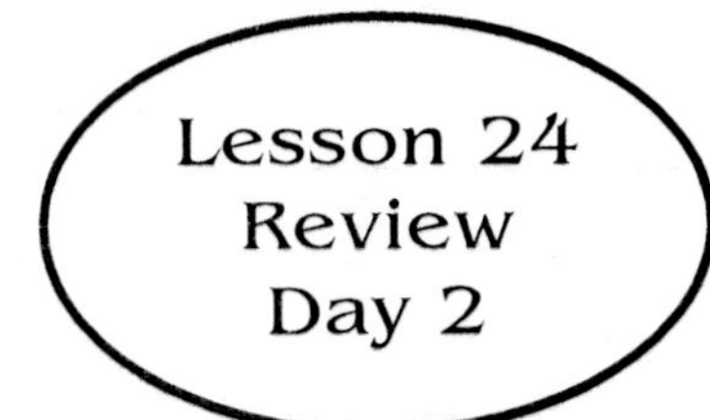

Date: ____________________

Review of Using Adjectives and Adverbs to Describe

A. Use your own **adverbs** or **adjectives** to complete each sentence below. Some sentences need an adverb, and some need an adjective.

1. Vicky walked ____________________.
2. The ____________________ piece of wood was rotten.
3. Jolie bought a ____________________ car.
4. Is that ____________________ sweater hers?
5. I ran ____________________ to win the race.
6. The ____________________ wind was howling.
7. I ____________________ smelled the flower.
8. It was a dark and ____________________ night.
9. Steve hurt his arm ____________________.
10. Mom removed the pants from the ____________________ box.
11. The television ____________________ went blank.
12. We wondered what happened to the ____________________ dog.

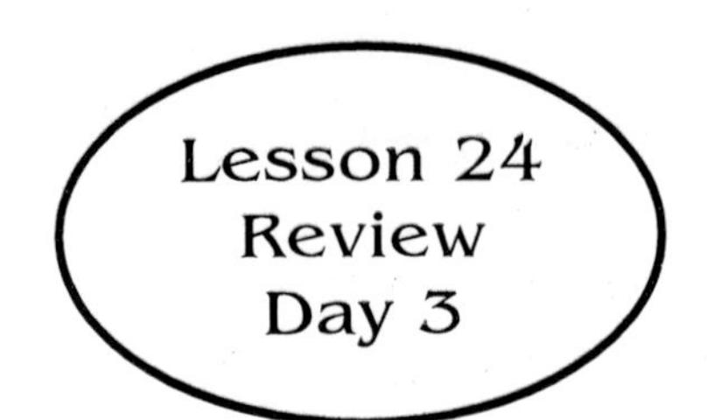

Date: ____________________

Review of Comparisons

A. Write an **X** on the line of each sentence that uses comparative words correctly.

1.____ This cheese smells better than that cheese.

2.____ Cake is sweeter than olives.

3.____ This rock is much harder than a piece of chalk.

4.____ Tonight is the most darkest night.

5.____ Did she sing longer than you?

6.____ That dress is brighter than the sun.

7.____ That watch ticked the loudest of any I have ever heard.

8.____ We ate faster today than yesterday.

9.____ Belinda wore the nicer dress I have ever seen.

10.____ Brad's dog barked most loudly than the other dogs.

11.____ That old ball was flatter than the new ball.

12.____ The new store is tiniest than the old store.

13.____ Debra was more embarrassed than Kathy.

14.____ The weather is most wet today.

15.____ It snowed heavier today than it did last week.

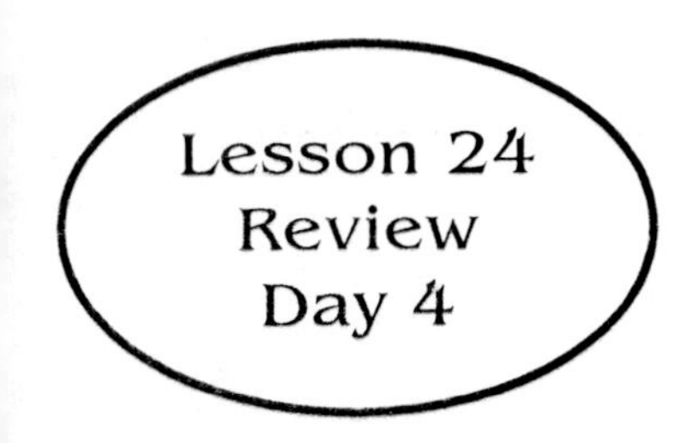

Date: ____________________

Review of Descriptive Writing

Think of a **main topic** for a descriptive story that has **one** paragraph. You can tell about **going to an amusement park**, **going to an animal shelter**, or think of a **main topic of your own**. Conduct some **outlining** to develop the main topic and a **details** for your story.

A. Complete the rough outline for your descriptive writing assignment.

Rough Outline

Main Topic: ____________________

Details: ____________________

Date: ____________________

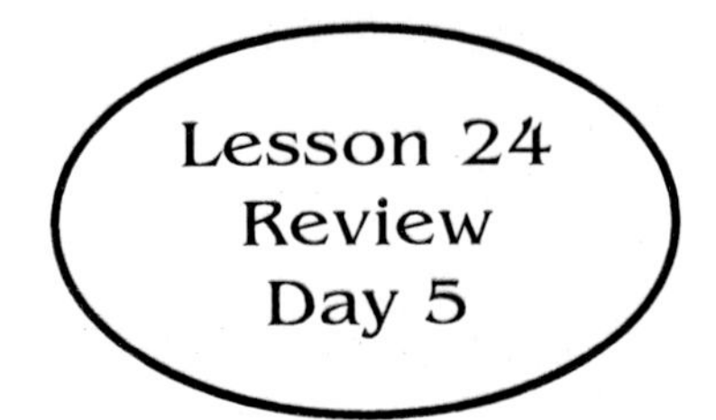

Review of Descriptive Writing

A. Use the rough outline you made on Day 4 of this lesson to complete a **final outline** for your story.

It will not be necessary in this lesson to write a draft of your paragraph.

Final Outline

Topic Sentence:

Detail Sentences:

Ending Sentence:

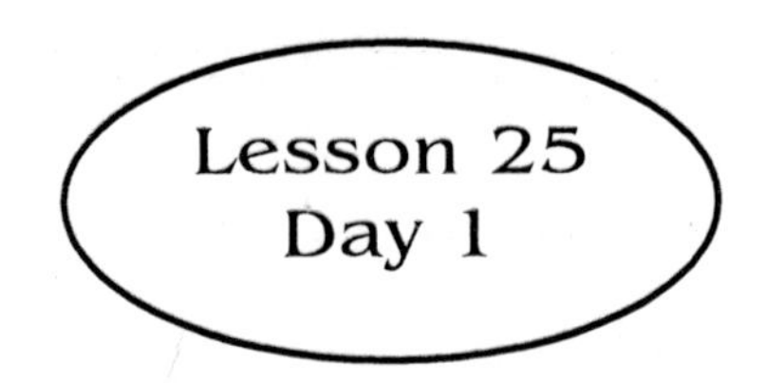

Date: ______________________

Persuasive Writing Introduction

A **persuasive writing** is one that tries to convince or persuade someone to do something, to believe in something, or to agree with the writer's opinion. There are many different types of persuasive writings which we will learn about in future lessons.

Usually the writer gives several arguments which support his position. A persuasive writing can include both facts and opinion. A fact is something that can be proven. On the other hand, an opinion cannot be proven as it is merely one person's feeling about something.

A persuasive story is arranged the same as any other story, although the content of the introductory and concluding paragraphs are slightly different than other stories.

- **Introductory Paragraph:** This is where the writer tells his audience what he is trying to convince them to agree with, believe in, or do.
- **Subtopic(s):**
  - Topic Sentence: This sentence tells about the main topic of the paragraph.
  - Detail Sentences: These sentences are where the writer gives the details of his argument. These sentences should support and agree with the introductory sentence. The writer should use descriptive words (adjectives) to express his position.
  - Ending Sentence: This sentence restates the topic sentence or summarizes the detail sentences of the paragraph.
- **Concluding Paragraph**: The writer uses this paragraph to summarize his arguments made in the subtopics. The writer also uses this paragraph to make one last plea to the reader to try and persuade him.

1. What is a persuasive story?

   a. A story that tells about someone's life.

   b. A story that only presents facts.

   c. A story that tries to convince someone.

   d. A story that explains how to do something.

2. Are persuasive stories arranged similarly to other stories?

   ___ **Yes**

   ___ **No**

3. What is the goal of a good persuasive story?

4. What is the introductory paragraph of a persuasive story supposed to do?

   a. It is where the writer tells his audience what he is trying to convince them to agree with, believe in, or do.

   b. It convinces the readers to do or believe something.

   c. It matches the concluding paragraph exactly.

   d. It makes one last plea to convince the reader.

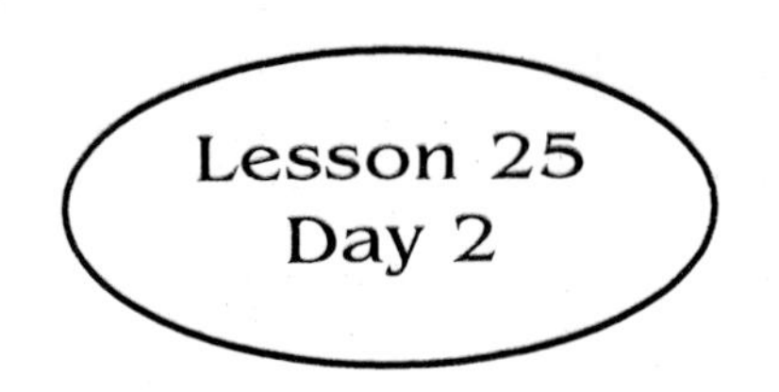

Date: ______________________

Persuasive Writing Introduction

A. Read the following persuasive story and answer the questions.

I think vacationing in Hawaii would be one of the best experiences ever. There are so many things to do, and it has the best weather in the United States. I think everyone should visit Hawaii at least once during their life.

In my opinion, Hawaii has the best weather of any place in the United States. The average temperature in Hawaii is 85 degrees in the summer and 78 degrees in the winter. These steady temperatures throughout the year make for a very consistent climate. It never snows in Hawaii and there is rarely a tornado or hurricane.

There are so many interesting places to visit in Hawaii. You can visit Pearl Harbor where several military artifacts are on display from World War II, or you can visit the Kilauea volcano which is constantly erupting. How often do you get a chance to see an active volcano? There are also several things to do in the national parks of Hawaii. Of course when you get tired you can always relax on Waikiki Beach. If you do not want to relax, you can always try your luck at surfing.

Visiting Hawaii would be a once in a lifetime experience. With the sun, the surf, and so many things to do, Hawaii is where you should visit if you ever get the chance.

1. Where does the writer want you to visit?

2. Which place is not a place in Hawaii to visit?
   a. Kilauea Volcano
   b. Waikiki Beach
   c. The Grand Canyon
   d. Pearl Harbor

3. How is the weather in Hawaii?
   a. It's always cold there.
   b. It always snows there.
   c. Tornadoes happen a lot.
   d. It has the best weather in the United States.

4. What can you do on Waikiki Beach?
   a. play charades
   b. surf
   c. buy a hot dog
   d. roller skate

5. Are there any national parks in Hawaii?

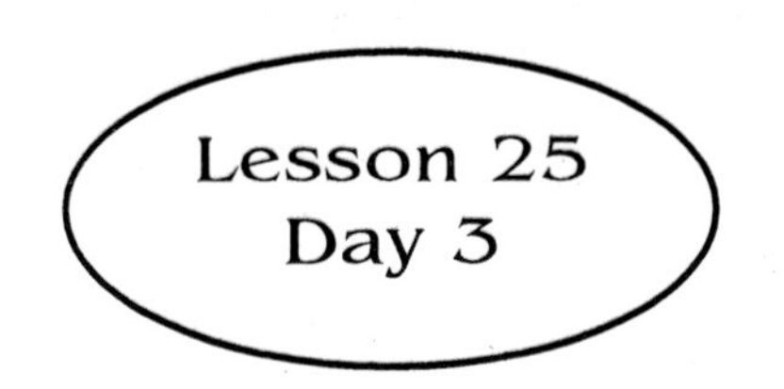

Date: ____________________

Persuasive Writing Introduction

A. On Day 1 of this lesson you learned what an introductory paragraph is supposed contain. Read the sample introductory paragraphs below and circle the best one.

1. Birds are fun to watch fly around. They all look so graceful as they soar through the air. All birds that can fly are amazing. I think birds are my favorite kind of animal.

2. Uncontrolled hunting of some birds of prey for several decades has put them on the endangered species list. We must do everything in our power to save these beautiful birds.

3. Birds of prey can be very pretty. Some of them have interesting hunting habits. I once saw a bald eagle snatch a fish right out of the water. Bald eagles are my favorite bird of prey.

4. I once saw a falcon and a golden eagle fighting over a piece of food. It was quite a fierce battle. In the end, the golden eagle's size was simply too much for the falcon, and the falcon had to retreat.

B. Read the sample concluding paragraphs below and circle the best one to match the introductory paragraph you selected above.

1. Birds are fun to watch. They are truly graceful creatures. That is why they are my favorite kind of animal.

2. For all of the reasons listed above, birds of prey must be protected. We must do everything we can to assure that they repopulate and are eventually removed from the endangered species list.

3. Birds of prey can be beautiful. Some birds of prey are fierce fighters. That is why the bald eagle is my favorite.

4. Birds of prey often fight over food. The battles can be quite fierce.

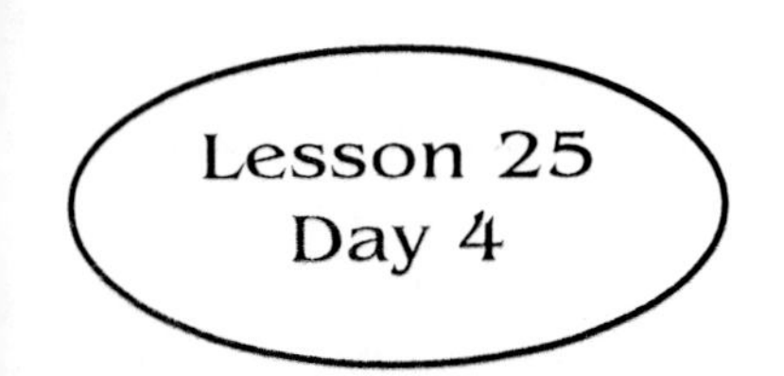

Date: ____________________

Persuasive Writing Introduction

A. Write an **<u>X</u>** by each sentence below that would be a suitable sentence if a writer were trying to convince readers that they should **not** own exotic animals like lions and tigers.

1. _____ Lions and tigers are wild animals and can never be trusted.
2. _____ They are too friendly to keep in a cage.

3. _____ No matter how tame they appear they are wild animals.
4. _____ Many owners of these animals have been injured by their pets.
5. _____ They are very expensive to feed.
6. _____ They can deter thieves from robbing your house.
7. _____ They can learn neat tricks when properly trained.
8. _____ These animals have teeth and claws that are very dangerous.
9. _____ No matter how well they are trained, their instincts tell them to be hunters.
10. _____ Their medical bills can become very expensive.

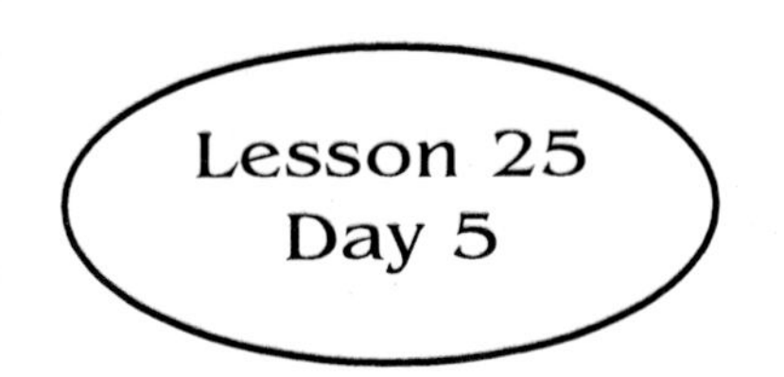

Date: ______________________

Persuasive Writing Introduction

A. Write a short persuasive introductory paragraph. Assume that you have taken the position that **all aluminum cans should be recycled in order to help the environment**. You will not have to outline for this exercise.

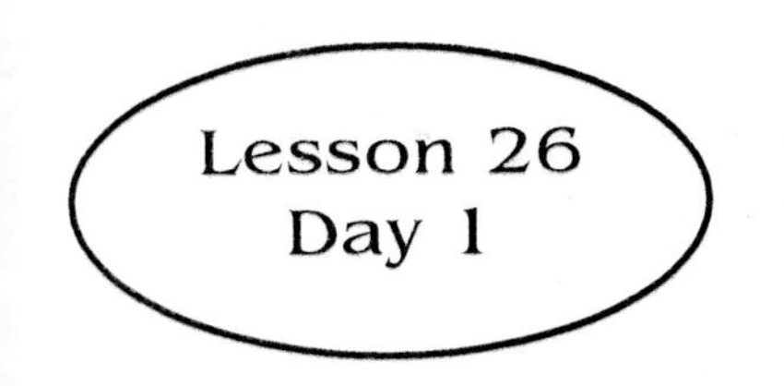

Date: ____________________

Persuasive Writing Using Your Voice

Of course you have already learned that a **persuasive story** is one that tries to convince or persuade someone to do something, to believe in something, or to agree with the writer's opinion.

When you speak to another person, normally you use a happy, serious, or angry voice depending on your mood. Just like when you speak, when you write you also use a **voice** by using certain words and punctuation.

When writing you must always consider **what** you are writing and **to whom** you are writing. If your audience is a group of your friends, you might write **informally** with a **friendly voice**. On the other hand, if your audience is your school teacher, then it would probably be a good idea to write more **formally** with a more **serious voice**.

What is the difference between **formal** and **informal writing**? Informal writing is writing that **sounds** more like a casual conversation. A writer using informal language might use slang, abbreviations, funny words, jokes, or incomplete sentences. A formal writing style **sounds** formal since it does not use slang, abbreviations, funny words, jokes, or incomplete sentences.

- - - -

A. If you were trying to persuade your friends to go somewhere with you, what kind of voice would you use?

1. friendly

2. serious

3. angry

Date: ____________________

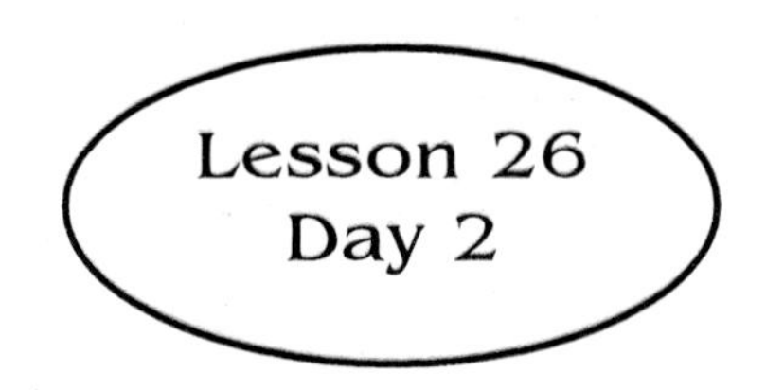

Persuasive Writing
Using Your Voice

When writing a persuasive letter the writer must always keep in mind his intended audience. Look at the two short letters below.

Dear Mayor Smith,

My name is Jason Pierce and I am eight years old. I would like to ask for your help in organizing a food drive for those who do not have enough food to eat this winter.

If we could ask the members of our town to donate at least one can of food to those who are less fortunate, everyone will have enough food to eat this winter.

I believe with your help we can make a difference and feed those people who are in need.

Best regards,

Jason Pierce

\- - -

Hi Mayor,

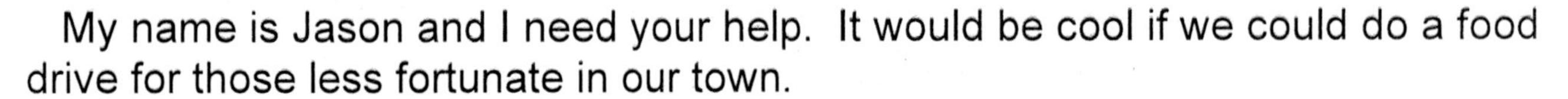

My name is Jason and I need your help. It would be cool if we could do a food drive for those less fortunate in our town.

It would totally rock if everyone would pitch in and donate to a food drive. That way, everyone remains happy with a full belly!

It would be awesome if we could ask everyone to donate at least one can of food to those less fortunate.

I would totally appreciate your help on this!

Thanks,

Jason

\- - -

A. With which letter do you think Jason will have a better chance of receiving the mayor's help?

1. __ first letter
2. __ second letter

Date: ____________________

Persuasive Writing Using Your Voice

A. Circle the correct answer for each question.

1. Go back and read the two sample letters from Day 2. What **voice** did Jason use in his first letter?
   a. serious voice
   b. funny voice
   c. angry voice
   d. nervous voice

2. What voice did Jason use in his second letter?
   a. serious voice
   b. friendly voice
   c. angry voice
   d. nervous voice

3. Why would the second letter likely not receive a favorable response from the mayor?
   a. because it is untruthful
   b. because Jason used the wrong voice and wrote too informally
   c. because the mayor is too busy
   d. because the letter did not make sense

4. Did Jason write formally or informally in his first letter?
   a. informally
   b. formally

5. Did Jason write formally or informally in his second letter?
   a. informally
   b. formally

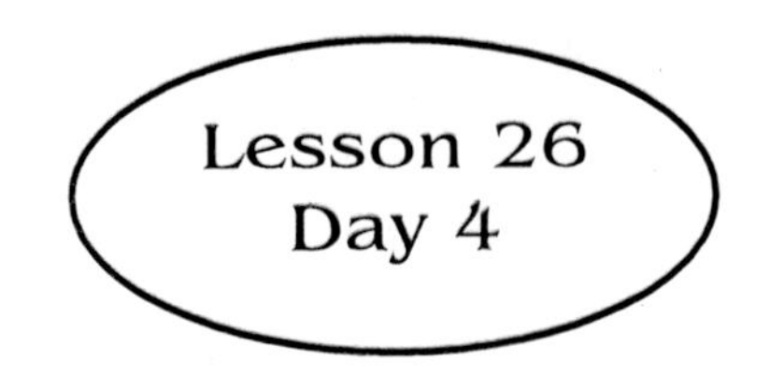

Date: ____________________

Persuasive Writing Using Your Voice

A. Assume you are unhappy with a recent purchase of a bicycle. You are going to write a **one** paragraph **persuasive** letter to the store owner where you purchased the bicycle. You would like for the owner to return your money. Conduct some outlining to gather your thoughts as to why you want the store owner to refund your money. You can use the outlines to organize your letter (rough and final outline forms are provided on the next two pages). Write a rough draft of your **one paragraph** letter below. What voice will you use? Will you use a formal or informal writing style?

Rough Outline

Main Topic:

Details:

Final Outline

Topic Sentence:

Detail Sentences:

Ending Sentence: (written after the topic sentence and detail sentences)

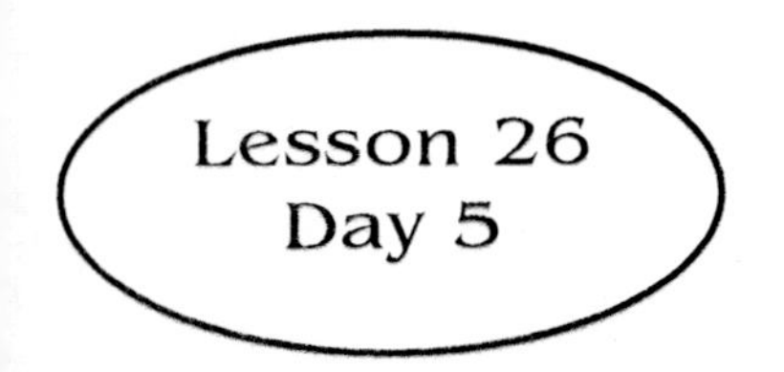

Date: ______________________

Persuasive Writing
Using Your Voice

A. Assume you are trying to persuade your friends to ride roller coasters with you at a local theme park. Conduct some outlining to gather your thoughts as to why you want your friends to go with you. You can use the outlines to organize your letter (rough and final outline forms are provided on the next two pages). Write a rough draft of your **one paragraph** letter below. What voice will you use? Will you use a formal or informal writing style?

Rough Outline

Main Topic:

Details:

Final Outline

Topic Sentence:

Detail Sentences:

Ending Sentence: (written after the topic sentence and detail sentences)

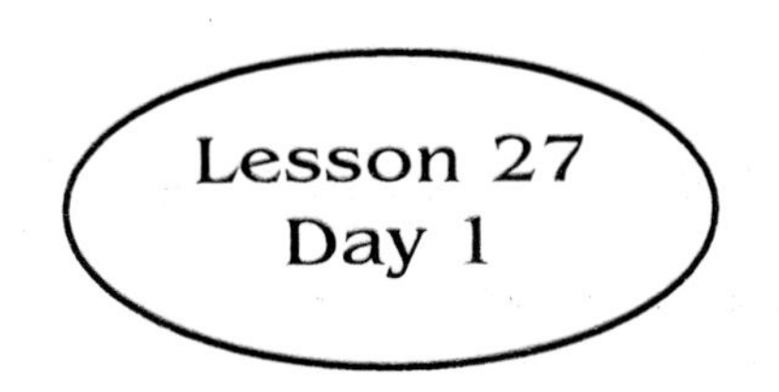

Date: ____________________

Persuasive Writing Advertisements

In addition to using your opinion to persuade someone to agree with your position, there are other ways to persuade people. One of the best places to look for examples of persuasive arguments is in advertisements.

Advertisements usually use one of the following methods of persuasion:

1) Everybody's got one or everybody's doing it

   "Howdy folks, this is happy Larry and I am here to tell you that everyone in your town either has one of these or will be buying one very soon. If you do not get one of these immediately, you will be the only person on your block to not have one."

2) Famous people use it, do this, or have one

   "This is Mr. Bigshot and he is a famous movie star. He uses our product and you should too. If it works for Mr. Bigshot it will definitely work for you!"

3) Just ask this person who has done it or had one

   "If you don't believe me, ask this person. He has been using our product for years."

4) Repeating something over and over

   "You need this car; this car is the best car available. You really need to buy this car. You would look fantastic in this car."

- - - -

A. Answer the questions below about this advertisement.

"Hi folks, this is Big Ben from Classic Watches of Anytown, USA. Be the first in your area to own this new style of watch. Mr. Movie Star has been wearing one and he loves it; you will love it too."

1. What method did Big Ben use to try and persuade people?

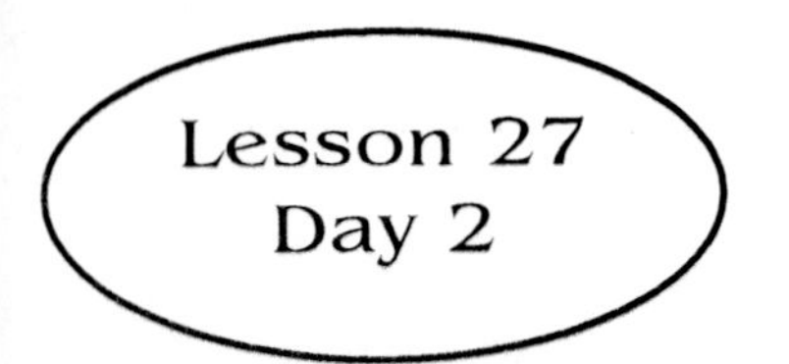

Date: ____________________

Persuasive Writing Advertisements

A. Answer each question below by finishing the sentence to make the kind of advertisement in parentheses.

1. Everyone in your class has one of these ___. (Everyone's Got One)
   a. you need to buy one too, immediately.
   b. everyone in your class has one.
   c. Famous Mr. Jones has one, and you should too.
   d. just ask your friend Mark, he has one.

2. Toy World is the best store in the world. Toy World has all of your favorite toys, and ___. (Repeating Something)
   a. everything is on sale.
   b. Toy World's prices will not be beat.
   c. Mr. Movie star shops here.
   d. all of your friends shop here, and so should you.

3. These new boots are special, ___. (Famous People)
   a. just ask Fred over here who wears them.
   b. everybody has them.
   c. and Mr. Movie star wears these boots; he loves them.
   d. all of your friends shop here, and so should you.

4. This book is the best book I've ever read, _____. (Ask the person who has one.)
   a. it's just the best book ever.
   b. everybody has bought a copy of it.
   c. and Mr. Movie star bought this book.
   d. just ask Beth here because she has read it.

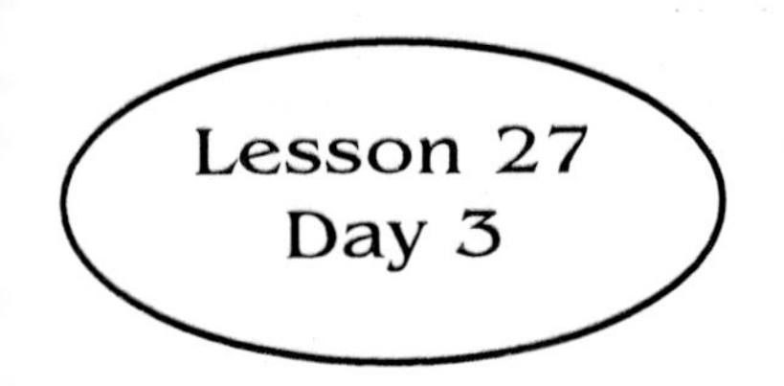

Date: ____________________

Persuasive Writing Advertisements

In addition to using the methods of persuasion on Day 1, many advertisers will use strong adjectives (Lesson 20) to describe their products. Read the sample advertisement below.

"I would like to tell you fine folks about our newest line of beautiful fuel-efficient cars. The beauty of these cars is more than skin deep. These beautiful fuel-efficient cars will not only get you where you're going for little money, but also will do so in style. These truly beautiful cars are so fuel-efficient that they will not hurt your wallet at the gas pump."

A. Answer the questions below.

1. What type of advertisement did this writer use?

____

2. What words did the writer emphasize in the above advertisement?

____

3. What are the two things the advertiser wants the reader to know about his cars?

a. ____

b. ____

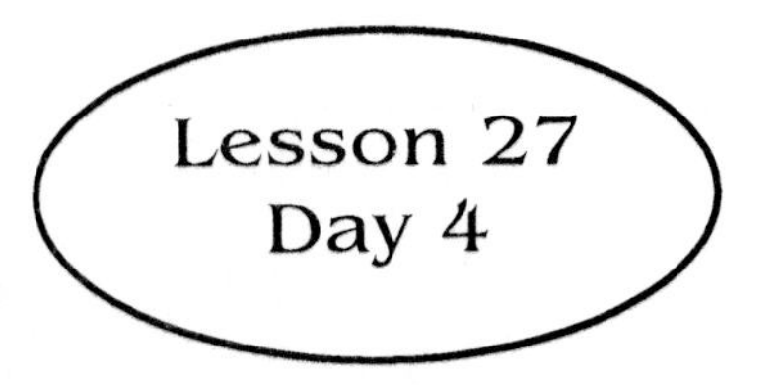

Date: ____________________

Persuasive Writing Advertisements

A. Choose one of the advertisement styles from Day 1 and write an advertisement about **a new hair care product**, **a new cupcake store**, or **an idea of your own**. Remember, you can use both **facts** and **opinion** to persuade your audience. What type of **voice** and **writing style** (formal or informal) will you use? Use some good **descriptive words** to describe your products or services. Conduct some outlining to gather your thoughts. Write a one paragraph advertisement. Outline forms are provided on the next two pages.

Rough Outline

Main Topic:

Details:

Final Outline

Topic Sentence:

Detail Sentences:

Ending Sentence: (written after the topic sentence and detail sentences)

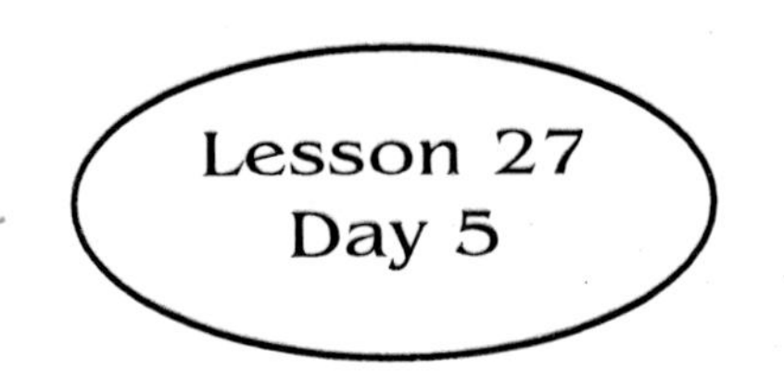

Date: ____________

Persuading Writing Advertisements

A. Choose a different advertisement style from Day 1 than you did on Day 4. Write an new advertisement for the idea you chose on Day 4. Remember, you can use both **facts** and **opinion** to persuade your audience. What type of **voice** and **writing style** (formal or informal) will you use? Use some good **descriptive words** to describe your product or services. Conduct some outlining to gather your thoughts. Write a one paragraph advertisement. Forms are provided on the next two pages.

Rough Outline

Main Topic:

Details:

Final Outline

Topic Sentence:

Detail Sentences:

Ending Sentence: (written after the topic sentence and detail sentences)

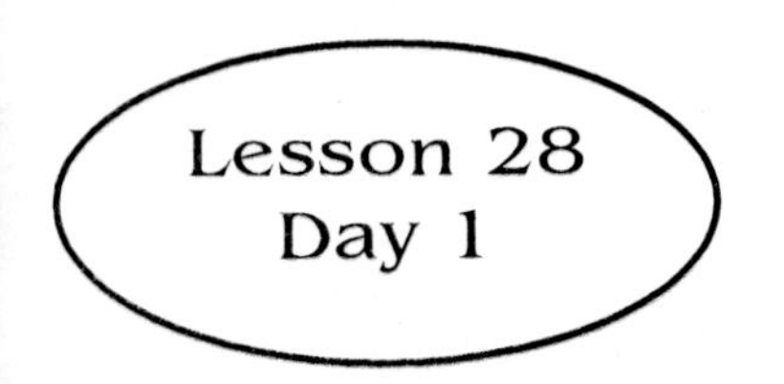

Date: ____________________

Persuasive Writing Reviews

A review is a type of persuasive writing that provides **both facts and opinion** of the writer. All reviews share the following two pieces of information:

1. (facts) The identity of what is being reviewed (place, movie, name, product, title, performer, author, or event).

2. (opinion) The opinion of the writer, whether or not he liked the thing being reviewed. A good review contains an explanation why the writer (reviewer) liked or disliked certain parts of the thing being reviewed.

- - - -

The following is a sample review for an automobile:

I recently had a chance to drive the new Mega Wagon by SuperCars, Inc. I was lucky enough to drive a brand new model that had never been driven before.

The Mega Wagon is a four door automobile that has room for six adults. The seats were very comfortable and the driver's controls were very well designed and easy to read. The materials for the upholstery seemed to be of a good quality. The fit and finish of the interior pieces seemed to be comparable to other cars in this price range.

The outside of the car was about average. The paint was of good quality but had a few minor imperfections. I personally am not crazy about the shape of the Mega Wagon, but others find it to be pleasing. The Mega Wagon also gets decent gas mileage (25 miles per gallon) for an automobile this size.

Overall, the new Mega Wagon is a good car for the money. It has a pleasant interior and a good quality outside. Although I do not find the new shape of the car to be pleasing, some people do. I encourage those of you who are looking for a good car at a fair price to take a look at this car.

A. Go back and underline the sentences that are facts about the Mega Wagon.

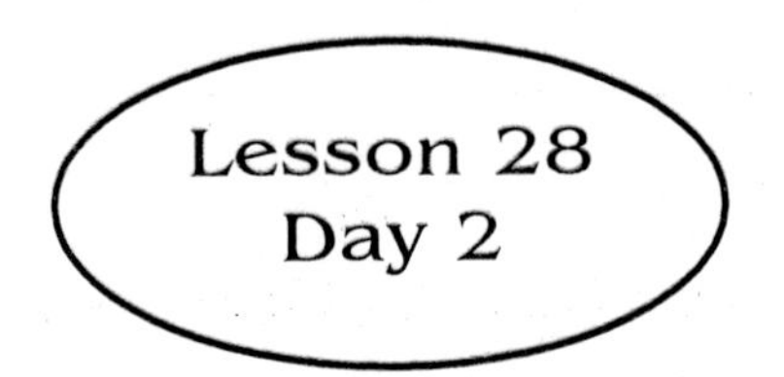

Date: ____________________

Persuasive Writing Reviews

A. Read the review from Day 1. Write an **X** next the each answer that is an opinion of the writer.

1.___ The Mega Wagon is a four door automobile.

2.___ The seats were very comfortable.

3.___ The Mega Wagon has room for six adults.

4.___ The driver's controls were very well designed and easy to read.

5.___ The materials for the upholstery seemed to be of a good quality.

6.___ The fit and finish of the interior pieces seemed to be comparable to other cars in this price range.

7.___ The outside of the car was about average.

8.___ The paint was of good quality but had a few minor imperfections.

9.___ The reviewer does not like the shape of the Mega Wagon.

10.___ The Mega Wagon gets 25 miles per gallon.

11.___ Overall, the new Mega Wagon is a good car for the money.

B. Think of a sentence that you could add to the review from Day 1. It can be another (made up) fact or just your opinion.

Date: ____________________

Persuasive Writing Reviews

A. Think of the last meal you ate. Think of three **facts** to write about as a review of the meal. Try to write complete sentences.

B. Think of the last meal you ate. Think of three **opinions** to write about as a review. Try to write in complete sentences. Be nice if it was your Mom who last cooked for you.

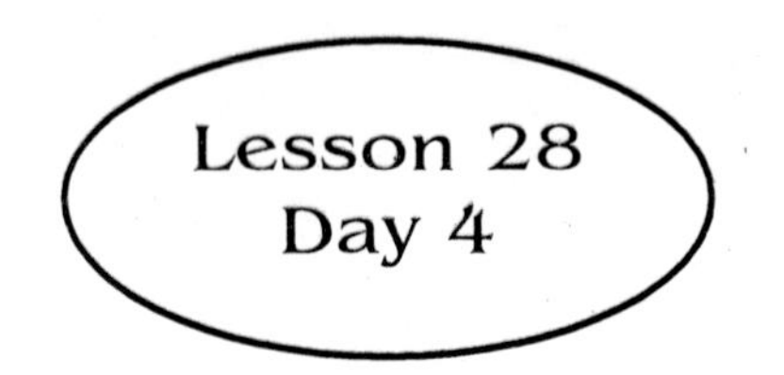

Date: ____________________

Persuasive Writing Reviews

A. Write a **book review**. Remember to use both **facts** and **opinion** to persuade your audience. Use **descriptive words** to describe a portion of the plot, characters, and setting. You should use a pleasant **voice** and a formal **writing style**.

Conduct some outlining to gather your thoughts. A rough outline and a final outline have been provided on the next two pages. You may use the final outline to organize your paragraph.

Rough Outline - Book Review

Main Topic:

Details:

Final Outline - Book Review

Topic Sentence:

Detail Sentences:

Ending Sentence: (written after the topic sentence and detail sentences)

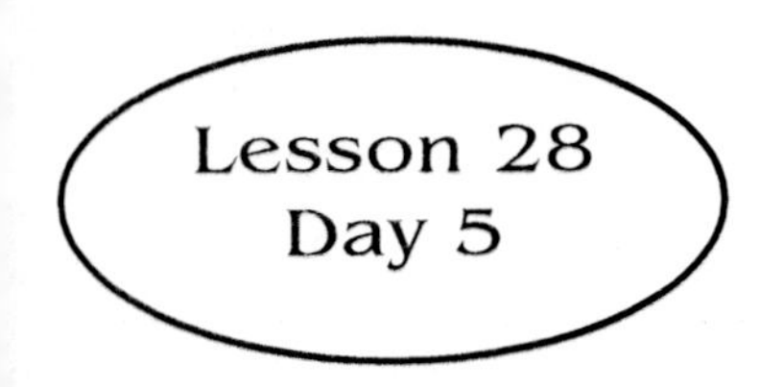

Lesson 28
Day 5

Date: ____________________

Persuasive Writing Reviews

A. Write a **movie review**. A movie review includes **facts** about the movie's plot, the actors, and perhaps the setting for the movie. The review should also include other facts such as the name of the director, the rating for the movie, where the movie is playing, and the length of the movie.

The review should tell just enough about the movie to inform the reader what the movie is about, but it should not give away key parts that might spoil the turning point for potential movie goers. The review should also include the reviewer's opinion of the plot, as well as the other aspects of the movie. The reviewer should use a persuasive voice to convince others that the movie is or is not worth viewing.

Conduct some outlining to gather your thoughts. A rough outline has been provided for you at the end of this lesson. You may use the final outline at the end of this lesson to organize your paragraph.

Rough Outline - Movie Review

Main Topic:

Details:

Final Outline - Movie Review

Topic Sentence:

Detail Sentences:

Ending Sentence: (written after the topic sentence and detail sentences)

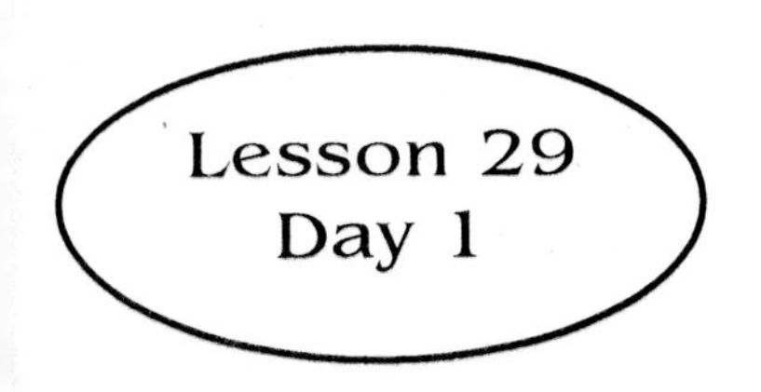

Persuasive Writing Letter to the Editor

In this lesson you will learn how to write a **three** paragraph **letter to the editor**. A letter to the editor is one that is directed to an editor of a magazine or newspaper. This type of letter expresses the opinion of the writer for almost anything that is on the writer's mind. Here is a sample of a letter to the editor.

> Dear Editor,
>
> I've wanted to write to you for quite some time to address a serious problem we have in our city, our sidewalks.
>
> Our sidewalks were first installed over fifty years ago. Given the harsh climate we live in, our sidewalks have suffered many decades of freezing and thawing. As you probably know, it is this continuous cycle of freezing and thawing that causes them to crack. Over the years, our sidewalks have become so cracked and broken that they are unusable in some areas of our town.
>
> I recommend that any other readers who feel the same way I do should write the mayor and express their concerns. If enough of us voice our concern, perhaps something will be done to fix this problem.
>
> Best regards,
>
> Mr. Si DeWalke

The contents of a letter to the editor are arranged similarly to other stories and letters, but the contents of the introductory and concluding paragraphs of a letter to the editor are slightly different than other types of stories/letters/writings. The introductory paragraph tells the editor why the author is writing the letter. The concluding paragraph is used to make one last plea to the reader to agree with his position.

A. Write a letter to the editor that discusses the **leash law**. Do you think people should have to put their dog on a leash when they go for a walk? If so, why? Do you think the leash law is a bad idea? If so, why? Remember to use both **facts** and **opinion** to persuade your audience. Conduct some outlining to gather your thoughts. The outlining information is below.

We will now start the writing process for a **letter to the editor** (persuasive writing).

Outlining Process
- A. Complete the rough outline
- B. Complete the final outline

Drafting Process
- A. Complete the rough draft
- B. Edit the rough draft
- C. Complete the final draft

Outlining Process

We will now begin your letter to the editor (persuasive writing) assignment with the outlining process. Outlining is the process where information about the writing is gathered in order to complete a rough outline and a final outline.

The entire outlining process is explained in **Appendix B**. If you need help in completing the rough outline or the final outline, use Appendix B. Whether or not you use Appendix B, you still need to complete the rough outline and the final outline in this lesson.

Complete the rough outline

Rough Outline

Main Topic:

Subtopic #1:

Details:

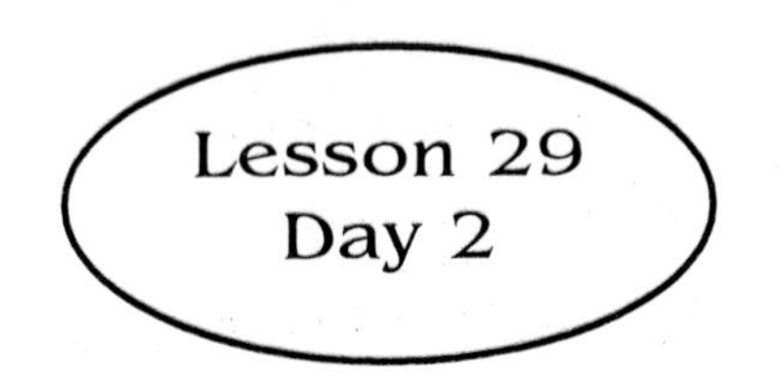

Date: ____________________

Persuasive Writing
Letter to the Editor

Complete the final outline

Final Outline

Introductory Paragraph:

Subtopic #1:

Topic Sentence:

Detail Sentences:

Ending Sentence: (written after the topic sentence and detail sentences)

Concluding Paragraph:

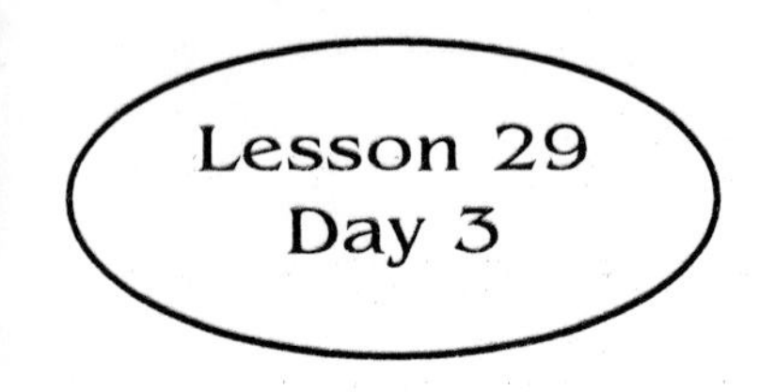

Date: ____________________

Persuasive Writing Letter to the Editor

Drafting Process

<u>Complete the rough draft</u>

So far you have spent quite a bit of time filling out the rough outline and the final outline. As a result, your final outline has all of the necessary pieces to complete your writing.

If you think of something you want to add while you are writing your rough draft, please do so. The final outline will now be used as a guide to write a rough draft.

Start by writing your **introductory paragraph**, sentences for each **subtopic** (topic sentence, detail sentences, and ending sentence), and **concluding paragraph** on the lines below.

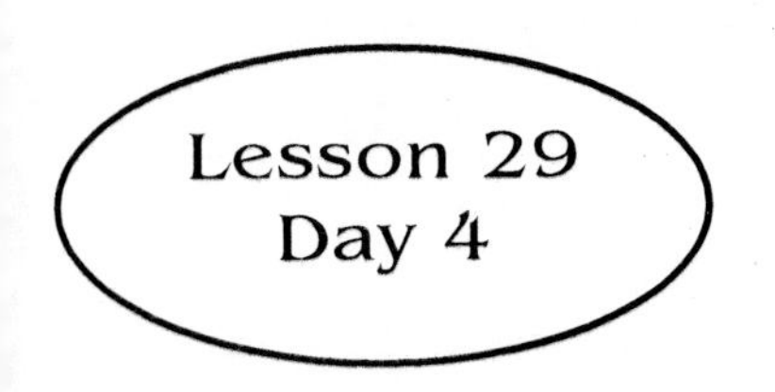

Date: ____________________

Persuasive Writing
Letter to the Editor

Edit the rough draft

It is now time to **edit** the rough draft you wrote on Day 3. Use the editing marks shown in **Appendix C** to correct any mistakes.

Do your paragraphs say what you want them to say? Do the words you chose make sense?

Look for and fix the following errors: 1) incorrectly used, misspelled, or misplaced words, 2) incorrect or missing spacing, 3) incorrect, missing, or misplaced punctuation, and 4) incorrect or missing capitalization.

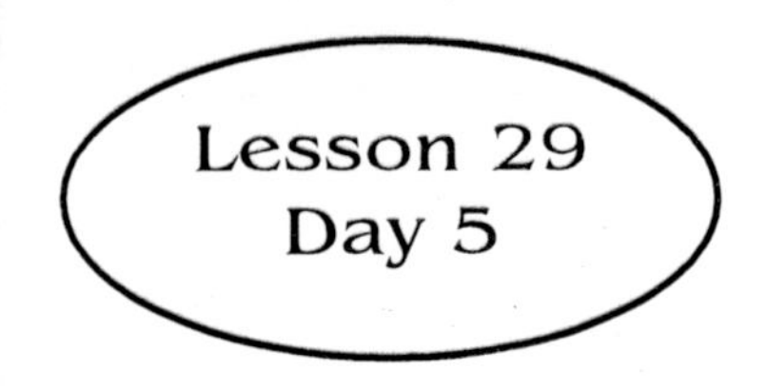

Date: ____________________

Persuasive Writing
Letter to the Editor

<u>Complete the final draft</u>

On Day 4 you edited your paragraphs. Today you will rewrite your paragraphs in their final draft form.

Read your paragraphs one more time. Do your sentences flow well from one to the other? Does your entire story make sense? Can you make it even better by adding 1) **time order words**, 2) **strong verbs**, 3) **adverbs**, 4) **exact nouns**, or 5) **descriptive adjectives**? Rewrite your edited paragraphs below.

Date: ____________________

Review of Persuasive Writing Introduction

A. Write an **X** by each sentence below that would be a suitable sentence if a writer were trying to convince readers that they should do certain things to stay healthy.

1.___ A balanced diet is good for your health.

2.___ Ice cream is a delicious snack.

3.___ Eating cake is fun at birthday parties.

4.___ Watching your calorie consumption will help control your weight.

5.___ Vegetables are an important part of your diet.

6.___ Snacking between meals can be harmful to your weight.

7.___ Fruits are a healthy kind of food to eat.

8.___ Foods that are high in fat content usually taste good.

9.___ Along with eating well, exercise is an important part of staying healthy.

10.___ It is a good idea to eat a candy bar after each meal.

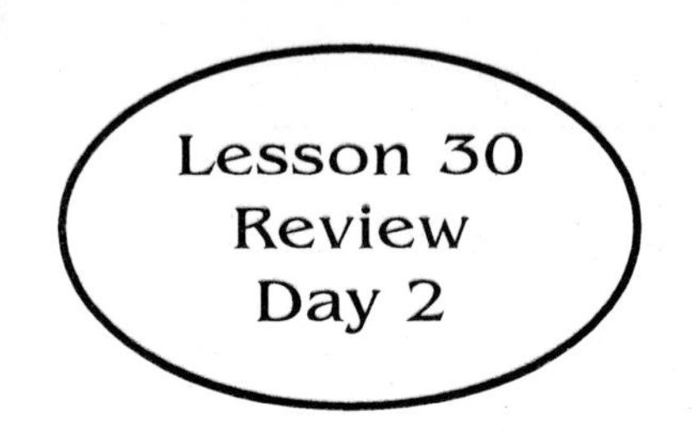

Date: ____________________

Review of Persuasive Writing - Using Your Voice

Hi everyone,

How's it going today? I'm just sitting here takin' it easy. How have y'all been doin? We need to get together real soon. Enjoy the day!

Later,

Lisa

\- - - - - -

A. Answer the following questions about the note above.

1. Read the short note above. What voice did Lisa use?

   a. serious voice

   b. angry voice

   c. friendly voice

   d. nervous voice

2. Do you think the people who received the note from Lisa know her?

   a. Yes, because she is using a friendly voice.

   b. No, because she was using slang.

   c. Yes, because she used the word y'all.

3. Did Lisa write formally or informally?

   a. informally

   b. formally

Date: ____________________

Review of Persuasive Writing - Advertisements

A. Answer each question below by finishing the sentence to make the kind of advertisement in parentheses.

1. Don't be the last person to buy one, ___. (Everyone's Got One)

   a. we are running out of them.

   b. everyone in your class has one.

   c. don't be the last person.

   d. Mr. Movie Star has one.

2. Choice Pickles are the best. Choice Pickles are crunchy, and ___. (Repeating Something)

   a. cheap.

   b. Choice Pickles are sweet.

   c. they are my favorite.

   d. Mr. Movie Star eats them.

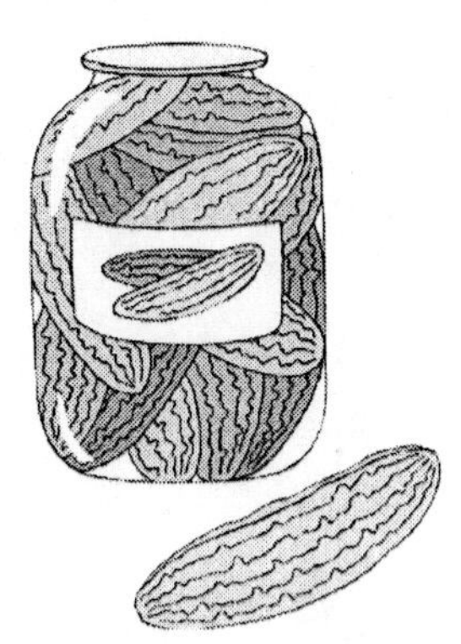

3. This purse is very nice, ___. (Famous People)

   a. your friend has one.

   b. just ask her, she bought one .

   c. Mrs. Movie carries one always.

   d. all of your friends bought one.

4. This Super Duper Oven works great, _____. (Ask the person who has one.)

   a. Mrs. Movie Star has one.

   b. everybody has it.

   c. the Super Duper Oven saves energy.

   d. just ask Mike here because he has one.

Date: ____________________

Review of Persuasive Writing - Reviews

I just saw the movie **Summer Fun** at the movie theater. It stars Mr. Movie Star and Mrs. Actress. Mr. Movie Star also starred in the movie **Winter Fun** that was a big hit last year. Summer Fun is also a good movie that tells the story of two travelers that drive around the country during the summer looking for fun.

One particular thing they did was work at a swimming pool as lifeguards for a day. It was very funny when Mr. Movie Star fell into the pool wearing all of his clothes.

I liked this movie although it did have a few slow moments. If you are looking for a movie to see this weekend and you want to laugh, this is the movie for you to see.

A. Read the above review. Write an **X** next the each answer that is an **opinion** of the writer.

1.___ Mr. Movie Star was in Winter Fun last year.

2.___ The two stars drive around the country.

3.___ Winter Fun was a big hit last year.

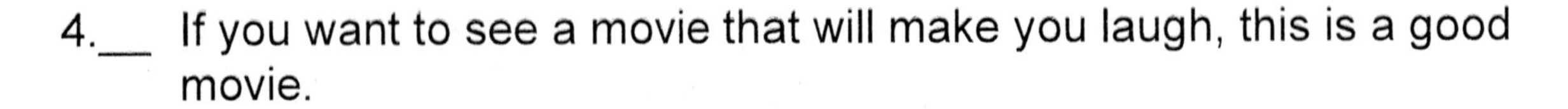

4.___ If you want to see a movie that will make you laugh, this is a good movie.

5.___ Mr. Movie Star fell into the swimming pool.

6.___ The writer of the review liked this movie.

7.___ This movie has a few slow moments.

8.___ Mrs. Actress was also in Summer Fun.

9.___ Summer Fun was a good movie.

10.___ The actors in the movie drove around during the summer.

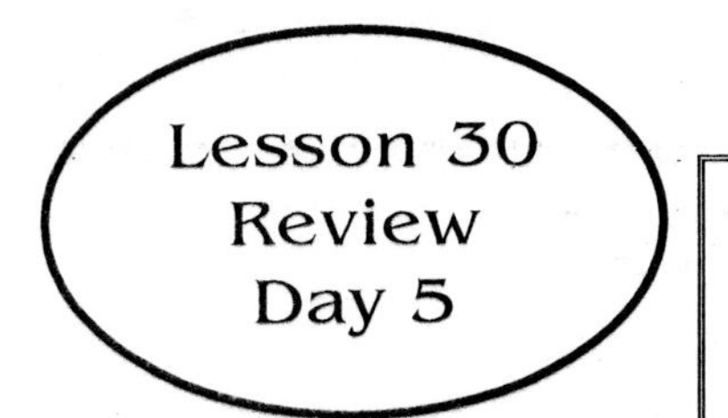

Date: ____________________

Review of Persuasive Writing - Letter to the Editor

A. Label the parts of the outline for a letter to the editor below:

-Outline-

- 1. ____________________: this is where the writer tells the editor why he is writing as well as his opinion on a particular idea.
- 2. ____________________:
  - o 3. ____________________: tells about the main topic of the detail sentences that follow.
  - o 4. ____________________: these sentences are where the writer provides the details of his argument. These sentences should support and agree with the topic sentence.
  - o 5. ____________________: this sentence restates the topic sentence or summarizes the detail sentences of the subtopic.
- 6. ____________________: the writer uses this paragraph to summarize his arguments made in **all** of the subtopics. The writer also uses this paragraph to make one last plea to the readers to agree with his positions.

Paragraph

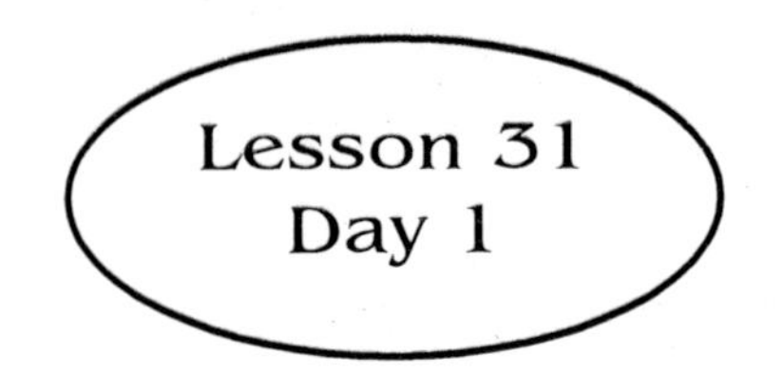

Date: ____________________

How-to Writing Introduction

A **how-to** writing explains to the reader how to complete a task. A typical how-to writing starts by telling the reader what materials, if any, are needed to accomplish the task. The remaining portion of a how-to writing explains the steps necessary to complete the task.

A how-to writing is different from a personal narrative or descriptive paragraph in that it does **not** focus on making the paragraph more interesting by adding descriptive words. Instead, a **how-to** writing only gives enough information to the reader to get something done. Here is an example of a how-to paragraph.

How to Paint a Picture

Painting pictures with oil paints is a lot of fun. First, you will need to make sure that you have a palette board and the required colors of paint. Next, make sure you have plenty of clean brushes. Of course you will also need a blank canvass on which to paint. Spread a color of paint on an artist's palette and begin the outline of your picture by using a thin brush. Make sure the outline is painted by using very thin and faint lines. Once completed, the outline will be used as a guideline to add colors and mixtures of colors from the palette. This is when your painting will become interesting. Of course, the types of brushes you use will also affect the result of your painting. Painting with oil paints is a lot of fun, but you have to use the correct materials and take the correct steps.

A. How is a **how-to** paragraph different than a narrative or descriptive paragraph?

B. List the items that are necessary to paint an oil painting.

1.

2.

3.

4.

C. To start the painting process, what is the first thing that gets painted?

1.

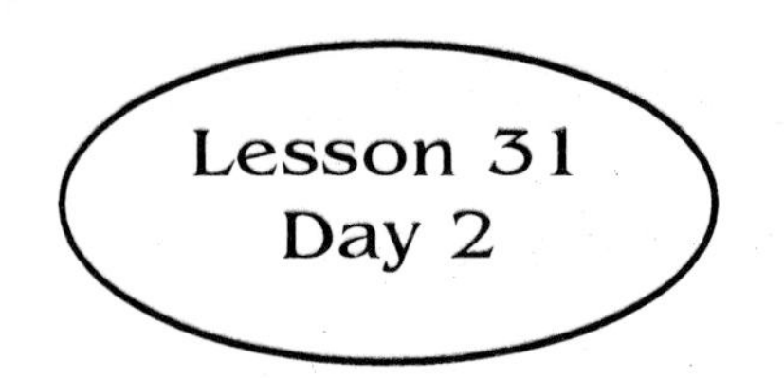

Date: ____________________

How-to Writing Introduction

A. Write an **X** on the lines next each story starter that could be made into a **how-to paragraph**.

1.____ directions to assemble a bicycle

2.____ a story about fishing with your Grandpa

3.____ a story about watching birds fly

4.____ how to assemble a model car

5.____ a story about your last birthday

6.____ steps required to take a picture

7.____ how to help with the laundry

8.____ a story about how you make homemade pasta

9.____ a story about a trip you took

10.____ a story about building a bird house

B. Write two more story starters of your own that could be used create a **how-to paragraph**.

a. ____

b. ____

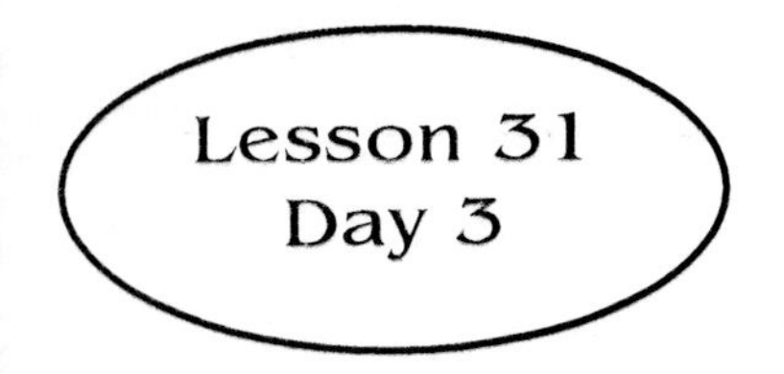

Date: ____________________

How-to Writing Introduction

A. Below are two story starters that act as **main topics** for a **how-to** paragraph. These main topics can be used to create **subtopics (steps)** for performing a task. Write three **subtopics (steps)** for each story starter below.

1. how to make toast

- ____________________
- ____________________
- ____________________

2. how to hit a baseball

- ____________________
- ____________________
- ____________________

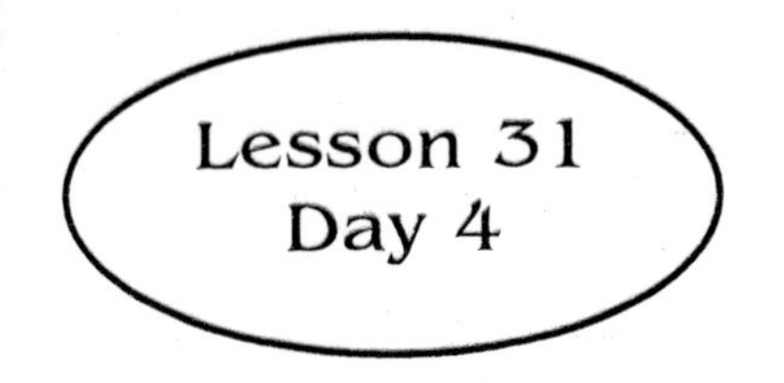

Date: ____________________

How-to Writing Introduction

A. Assume you have been asked to write instructions for **making a bowl of cereal**. Think of five steps (subtopics) that are required and write them below.

1. ____________________

2. ____________________

3. ____________________

4. ____________________

5. ____________________

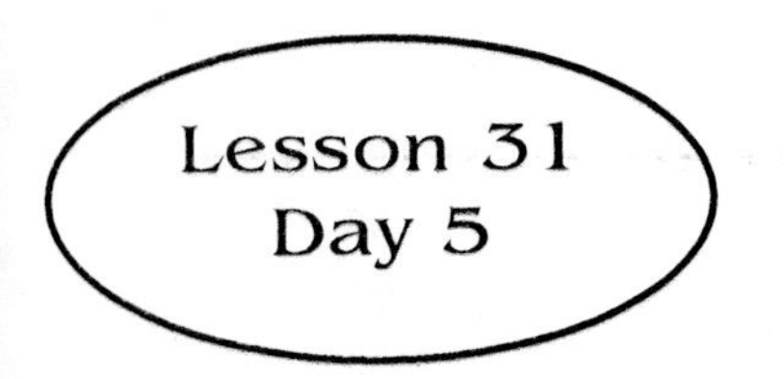

Date: ____________________

How-to Writing Introduction

A. Using the steps you created on Day 4, write a paragraph on how to make a bowl of cereal. For this exercise we will not need to conduct any outlining. Also, do not worry about adding an introductory or ending sentence.

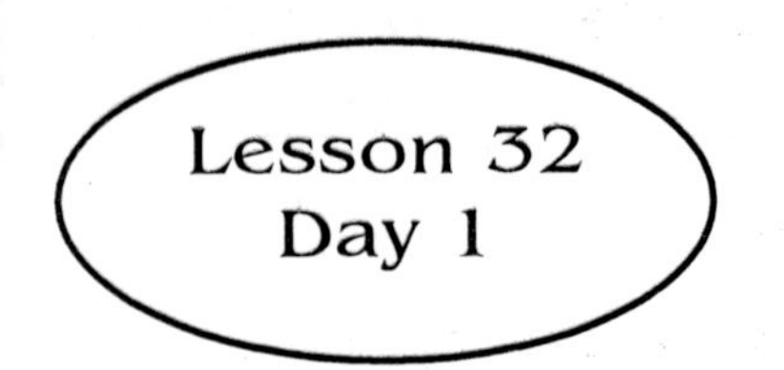

Date: ____________________

Cause and Effect

Cause and effect is a relationship between two things. One thing happens that causes something else to happen.

"Because this happened, it caused this to happen."

"Because I jumped into the pool, it caused a splash"
↑ Cause ↑ Effect

A. Match the **causes** and **effects** by drawing lines to connect them.

Cause	Effect
1. a match was struck	a. the girl got a skinned knee
2. the faucet was turned on	b. Molly answered the door
3. a girl fell down	c. the door was unlocked
4. the doorbell rang	d. the document printed
5. the computer sent the document to the printer	e. water poured out
6. the key was turned	f. a fire started

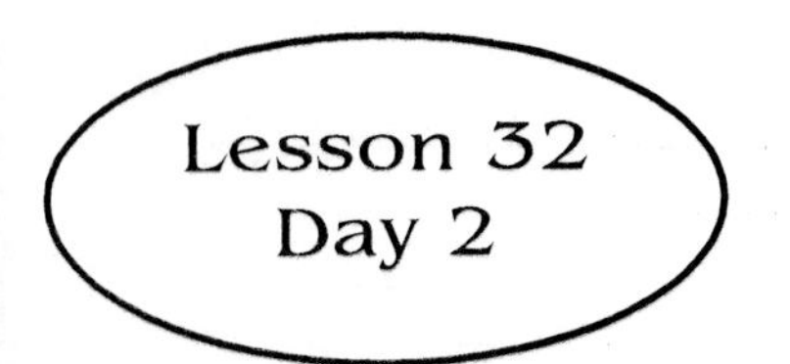

Date: ____________________

Cause and Effect

A. Read the paragraph below and answer the questions.

The alarm rang and Tina woke up. Her Mom called her and she went downstairs. Since there was no cereal left in the box, she had a piece of toast instead. Mom said her blue coat was dirty, so she had to wear her black coat. Because she was fully dressed, Tina was finally ready to leave the house.

1. What was the effect of the alarm ringing?

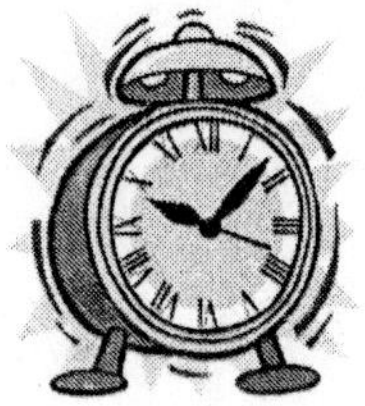

2. What caused Tina to wear her black coat?

3. What caused Tina to have toast?

4. What was the effect of Tina's Mom calling her?

5. What was the effect of Tina being fully dressed?

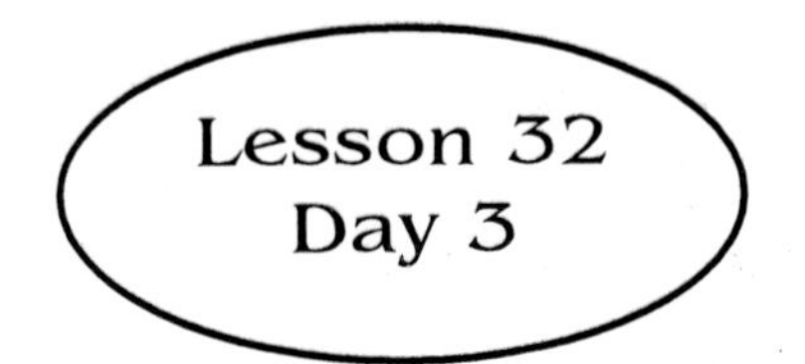

Date: ____________________

Cause and Effect

A. Think of three things you did yesterday that **caused** an **effect**. Write them below. Write sentences that show what happened.

Example: Because I hurt my foot, I could not walk.

1. ____

2. ____

3. ____

Date: ____________________

Cause and Effect

A. Fill in the missing **effects** on the table below. There is more than one correct answer for each.

Cause		Effect
1. It snowed.	←→	
2. The bus is late.	←→	
3. The button was pushed.	←→	
4. Jill ran fast.	←→	
5. I read the book.	←→	
6. The music played.	←→	

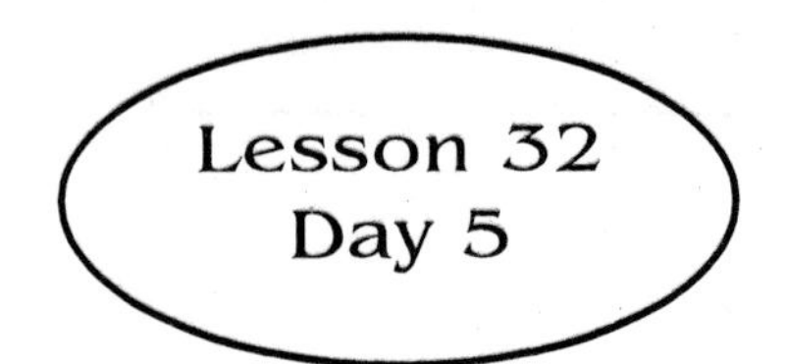

Date: ____________________

Cause and Effect

A. Fill in the missing **causes** on the table below. There is more than one correct answer for each.

Cause		Effect
1.____________________	←→	The glass shattered.
2.____________________	←→	The light turned on.
3.____________________	←→	The flower died.
4.____________________	←→	The baby was fed.
5.____________________	←→	The television turned on.
6.____________________	←→	The corn stalk grew.

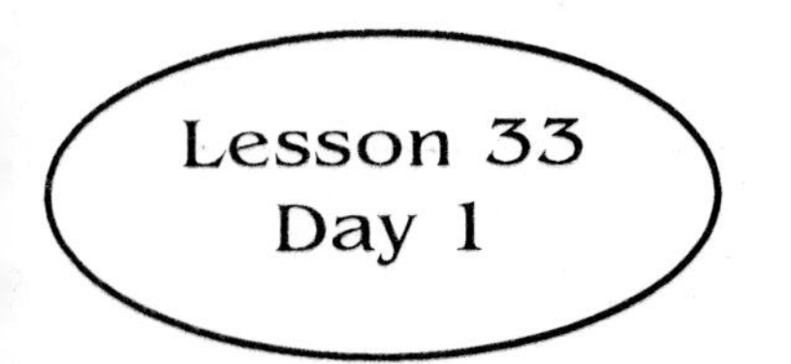

Date: ____________________

Giving Directions

Have you ever asked someone how to get somewhere? If that person told you how to get to the place, he was giving directions to you. What kinds of words do people use to give directions?

Generally there are four different types of words that are used, alone or in combination with each other, to give directions: **words of direction**, **words of distance**, **landmark words**, and an **address**.

Words of Direction

As the name states, **words of direction** are words that actually tell a person which way to go. Words of direction are those such as **turn**, **up**, **down**, **left**, **right**, **forward**, **backward**, **curve**, **next to**, **straight**, **ahead**, **U-turn**, **below**, **above**, **north**, **south**, **east**, **west**, **stop**, and **go**.

Many times, words of direction alone are not enough to provide the traveler with an accurate picture of where they need to go. Sometimes the traveler also needs to know how far to travel in a certain direction.

Words of Distance

As the name states, **words of distance** tell the traveler not which way to travel but instead how **far** to travel. Words of distance are words such as **meters**, **miles**, **blocks**, **yards**, **feet**, **inches**, and **millimeters**.

Landmarks

Along with words of direction and words of distance, **landmark** words can also be used to give directions. A landmark is **any** object that can be easily recognized by the traveler.

For example: Turn right by the **old red barn** on the left side of the road.
Can you see how the traveler might be able to know where to turn?

Address

An address is a **collection of words and numeric** information that acts to directly identify where something is located.

For example: 100 Main Street, Anytown, Indiana

A. Answer these questions about the directions below.

1. Assume Ed has asked his friend Sarah for directions to her house. Sarah tells Ed that she lives in the red house near the water tower of their hometown. Are these directions any good?

   a. No, it would be impossible to know where Sarah lives.

   b. Yes, but only if Ed knows where the water tower is in their town.

   c. No, because Sarah did not say how many miles to travel.

2. Assume Sarah has given her friend Ed the following two sets of directions:

   "I live in the red house near the water tower in our town."

   or

   "I live at 100 Maple Street, Anytown, California."

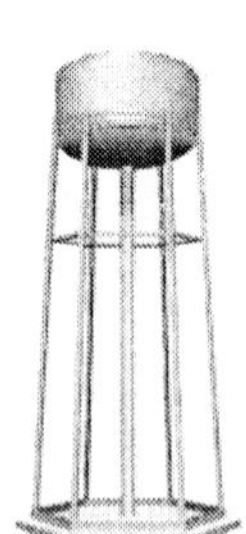

   Are both sets of directions helpful?

   a. Yes, both sets are very helpful.

   b. The first set of directions is much more helpful than the second set.

   c. It depends on whether or not Ed knows where the water tower is, and if he also knows how to get to 100 Maple Street.

   d. No, it would be impossible to find Sarah's house using either.

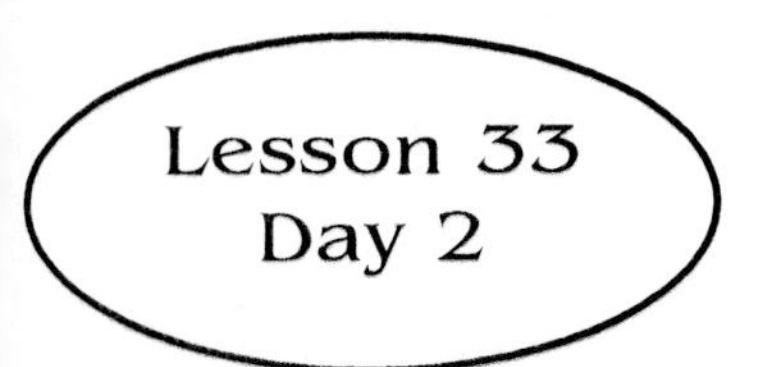

Date: ____________________

Giving Directions

A. Answer the questions about the following directions.

1. If you were to receive the following **directions**, where would you arrive?

   -Stand up.

   -Take three steps straight ahead.

   -Turn around and take four steps straight ahead.

   -Turn around again and take one step ahead.

   -Sit down.

   Look at the choices below. Circle the answer that describes where you arrived.

   a. You would be in the next room.
   b. You would be where you started.
   c. You would be in the kitchen.
   d. You would be somewhere different from where you started.

2. What is wrong with the following directions?

   Turn right on Main Street. When you reach Elm Street turn left.

   a. Nothing is wrong with the directions.
   b. You should have turned left on Elm instead of right.
   c. You have no idea which direction you were traveling when you were told to turn right on Main Street.
   d. You are pretty sure that Elm Street doesn't cross Main Street.

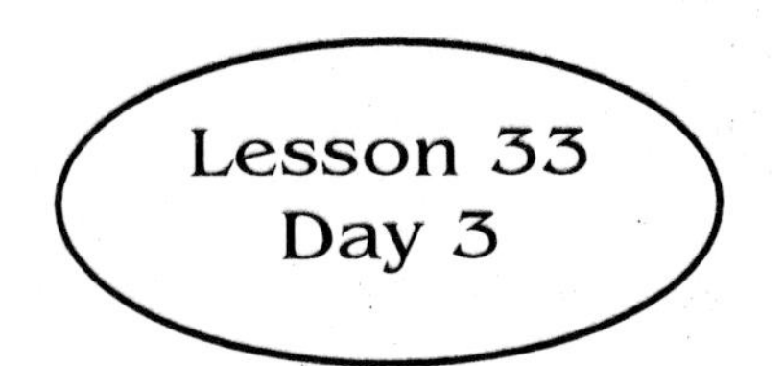

Date: ____________________

Giving Directions

Not only is it important to use sets of directions correctly, but also it is important to arrange your **directions** in **order**. If you give directions out of order, the traveler will never arrive at his destination. Remember, the words we use when something needs to be told in a **certain order** are **first**, **next**, **then**, and **finally**.

Title: How to Get to Grandma's House

-**First**, travel north on Main Street until you arrive at Elm Street.
-**Next**, turn right and travel straight ahead for one mile.
-**Then**, turn right and travel 240 feet.
-**Then**, turn right and travel 100 feet.
-**Finally**, turn right into Grandma's driveway.

- - - - - - -

A. Number the directions below in the correct order.

1. ___ Next, turn left at Pine Street.

2. ___ First, start at 100 Main Street. Turn left onto Main Street.

3. ___ Finally, turn right on Walnut Street and arrive at your destination of 400 Walnut Street.

4. ___ Then, go straight for two miles until you come to Walnut Street.

Lesson 33
Day 4

Date: ____________________

Giving Directions

A. Can you tell what is wrong with the following two sets of **directions**? Underline the correct answer in each group.

1. -First, drive on 1st Street until you see 4th Street.

   -Then, turn left on 4th Street and go straight for two miles.

   -Next, turn left on 3rd Street.

   -Finally, turn right on Bacon Street.

   a. 4th Street is not a real street.

   b. The directions do not use words of direction.

   c. The directions are out of order.

   d. The directions do not tell which direction to travel on 1st Street when starting.

2. -First, start at the intersection of South Street and Pine Drive. Drive south on South Street until you see the water tower.

   -Next, turn left at the water tower and travel for two miles.

   -Then, when you see the red barn, turn right and travel for one mile.

   -Finally, when you see the green car, turn left and travel on Linden Court for one mile until you reach your destination.

   a. The directions do not use landmarks.

   b. The directions are out of order.

   c. The directions do not use words of distance.

   d. There is nothing wrong with these directions.

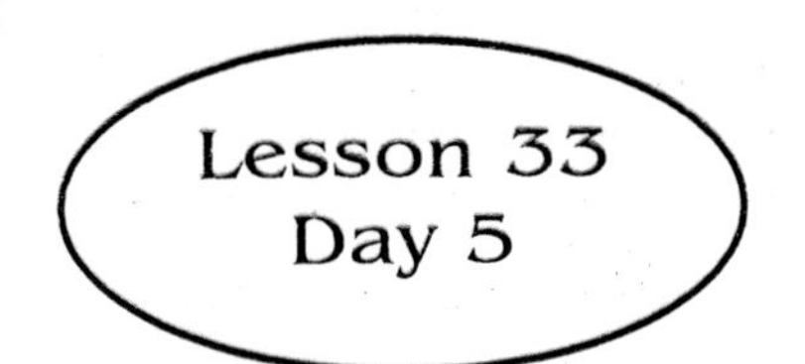

Date: ______________________

Giving Directions

A. Think of somewhere in your yard other than where you are sitting. Starting from where you are now, give **directions** to this other place in your yard. Remember to use **words of direction, words of distance,** and **landmarks** (if necessary). When you are done writing your **directions**, give them to someone in your family for testing to see if they work.

First, ______________________

Next, ______________________

Then, ______________________

Finally, ______________________

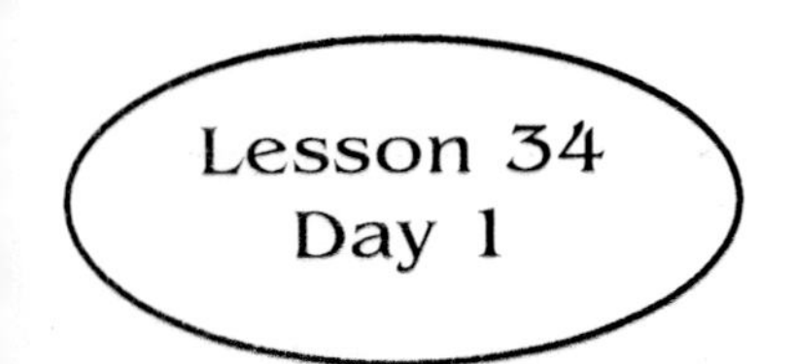

Date: ____________________

How-to Writing

As you learned in Lesson 31, a **how-to** writing explains to the reader how to complete a task. A typical how-to writing starts by telling the reader what materials, if any, are needed to accomplish the task. The remaining portion of a how-to writing explains the steps necessary to complete the task.

A how-to writing is different from a personal narrative or descriptive paragraph in that it does **not** focus on making the paragraph more interesting by adding descriptive words. Instead, a **how-to** writing only describes information for the reader to get something done.

A. Write a **three** paragraph writing about **how to fly a kite** (one introductory paragraph, one body paragraph, and one concluding paragraph). Remember to put your writing in the order in which the process occurs. Conduct some outlining to gather your thoughts. The outlining information is below.

We will now start the writing process for a **how-to writing**.

Outlining Process
  A. Complete the rough outline
  B. Complete the final outline

Drafting Process
  A. Complete the rough draft
  B. Edit the rough draft
  C. Complete the final draft

Outlining Process

We will now begin your how-to writing assignment with the outlining process. Outlining is the process where information about the writing is gathered in order to complete a rough outline and a final outline.

The entire outlining process is explained in **Appendix B**. If you need help in completing the rough outline or the final outline, use Appendix B. Whether or not you use Appendix B, you still need to complete the rough outline and the final outline in this lesson.

Complete the rough draft

Rough Outline

Main Topic:

Subtopic #1:

Details:

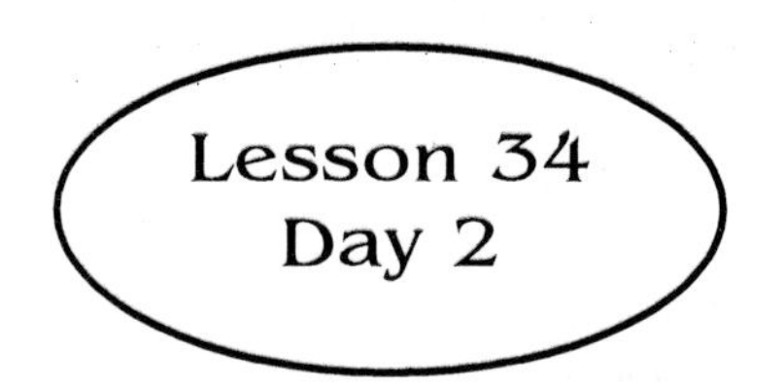

Date: ____________

How-to Writing

Complete the final outline

Final Outline

Introductory Paragraph:

Subtopic #1:

Topic Sentence:

Detail Sentences:

Ending Sentence: (written after the topic sentence and detail sentences)

Concluding Paragraph:

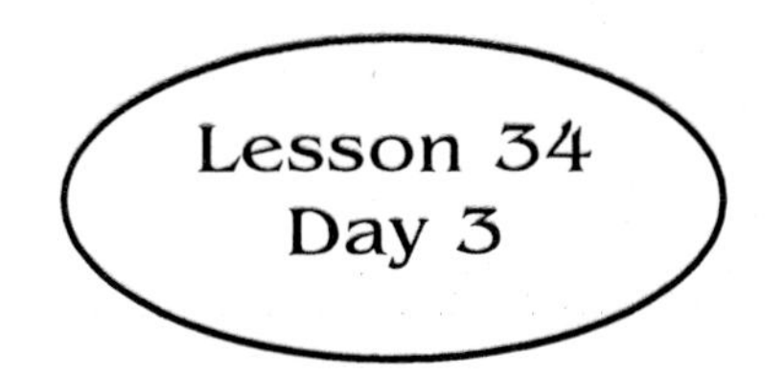

Date: ____________________

How-to Writing

Drafting Process

Complete the rough draft

So far you have spent quite a bit of time filling out the rough outline and the final outline. As a result, your final outline has all of the necessary pieces to complete your writing.

If you think of something you want to add while you are writing your rough draft, please do so. The final outline will now be used as a guide to write a rough draft.

Start by writing your **introductory paragraph**, sentences for each **subtopic** (topic sentence, detail sentences, and ending sentence), and **concluding paragraph** on the lines below.

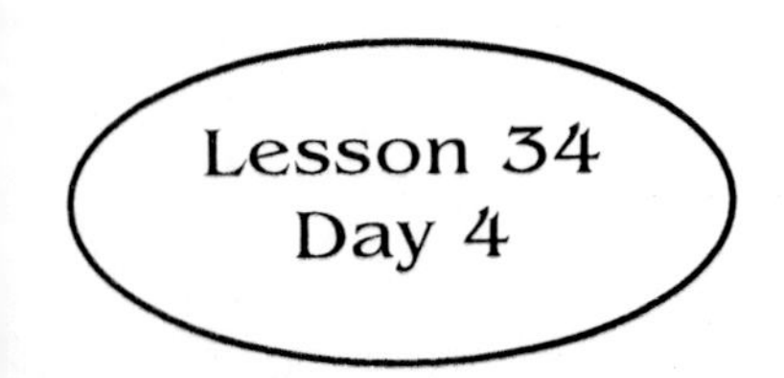

Date: ____________________

How-to Writing

Edit the rough draft

It is now time to **edit** the rough draft you wrote on Day 3. Use the editing marks shown in **Appendix C** to correct any mistakes.

Do your paragraphs say what you want them to say? Do the words you chose make sense?

Look for and fix the following errors: 1) incorrectly used, misspelled, or misplaced words, 2) incorrect or missing spacing, 3) incorrect, missing, or misplaced punctuation, and 4) incorrect or missing capitalization.

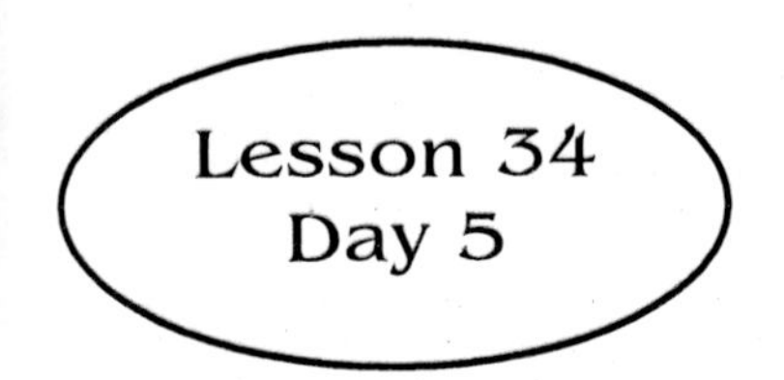

Date: ____________________

How-to Writing

Complete the final draft

On Day 4 you edited your paragraphs. Today you will rewrite your paragraphs in their final draft form.

Read your paragraphs one more time. Do your sentences flow well from one to the other? Does your entire story make sense? Can you make it even better by adding 1) **time order words**, 2) **adverbs**, or 3) **exact nouns**? Rewrite your edited paragraphs below.

Date: ____________________

How-to Writing

A. Write another **three** paragraph **how-to writing**. Come up with an idea of your own.

We will now start the writing process for a **how-to writing**.

Outlining Process
- A. Complete the rough outline
- B. Complete the final outline

Drafting Process
- A. Complete the rough draft
- B. Edit the rough draft
- C. Complete the final draft

Outlining Process

We will now begin your how-to writing assignment with the outlining process. Outlining is the process where information about the writing is gathered in order to complete a rough outline and a final outline.

The entire outlining process is explained in **Appendix B**. If you need help in completing the rough outline or the final outline, use Appendix B. Whether or not you use Appendix B, you still need to complete the rough outline and the final outline in this lesson.

Complete the rough outline

Rough Outline

Main Topic:

Subtopic #1:

Details:

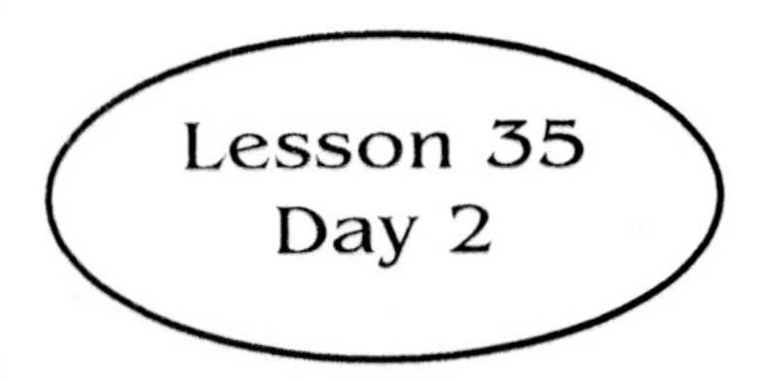

Date: ______________________

How-to Writing

Complete the final outline

Final Outline

Introductory Paragraph:

Subtopic #1:

Topic Sentence:

Detail Sentences:

Ending Sentence: (written after the topic sentence and detail sentences)

Concluding Paragraph:

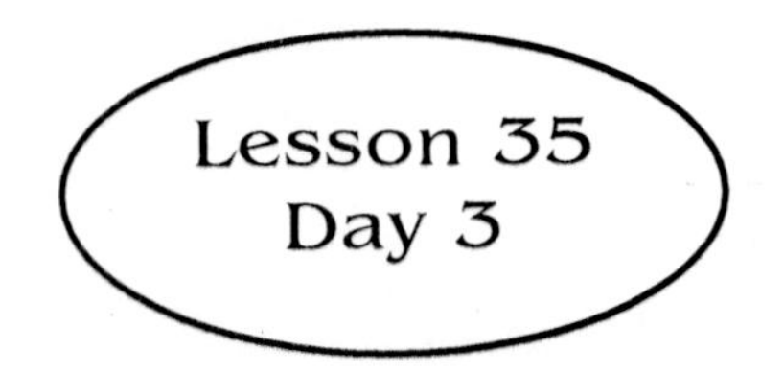

Date: ____________________

How-to Writing

Drafting Process

Complete the rough draft

So far you have spent quite a bit of time filling out the rough outline and the final outline. As a result, your final outline has all of the necessary pieces to complete your writing.

If you think of something you want to add while you are writing your rough draft, please do so. The final outline will now be used as a guide to write a rough draft.

Start by writing your **introductory paragraph**, sentences for each **subtopic** (topic sentence, detail sentences, and ending sentence), and **concluding paragraph** on the lines below.

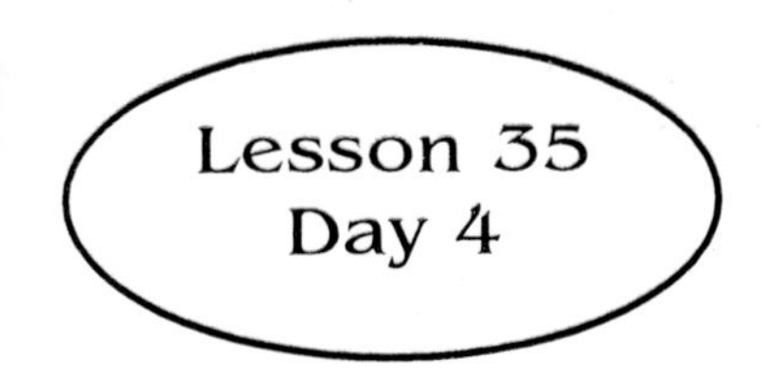

Date: ____________________

How-to Writing

Edit the rough draft

It is now time to **edit** the rough draft you wrote on Day 3. Use the editing marks shown in **Appendix C** to correct any mistakes.

Do your paragraphs say what you want them to say? Do the words you chose make sense?

Look for and fix the following errors: 1) incorrectly used, misspelled, or misplaced words, 2) incorrect or missing spacing, 3) incorrect, missing, or misplaced punctuation, and 4) incorrect or missing capitalization.

Date: ____________________

How-to Writing

Complete the final draft

On Day 4 you edited your paragraphs. Today you will rewrite your paragraphs in their final draft form.

Read your paragraphs one more time. Do your sentences flow well from one to the other? Does your entire story make sense? Can you make it even better by adding 1) **time order words**, 2) **adverbs**, or 4) **exact nouns**? Rewrite your edited paragraphs below.

Date: ____________________

Review of How-to Writing Introduction

A. Below are two story starters that act as **main topics** for a **how-to** paragraph. These main topics can be used to create **subtopics (steps)** for performing a task. Write three **subtopics (steps)** for each story starter below.

1. how to draw a picture

- ____________________
- ____________________
- ____________________

2. how to plant flowers

- ____________________
- ____________________
- ____________________

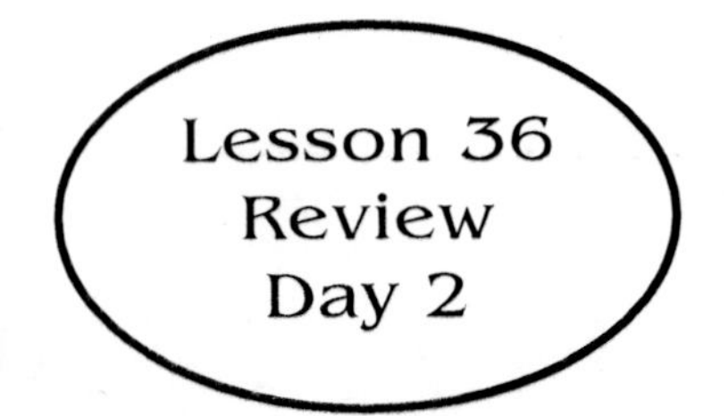

Date: ____________________

Review of Cause and Effect

A. Think of three things you did yesterday that caused an effect. Write them below. Write sentences that show what happened.

Example: Because I ate a snack, I was not hungry.

1. ____________________

2. ____________________

3. ____________________

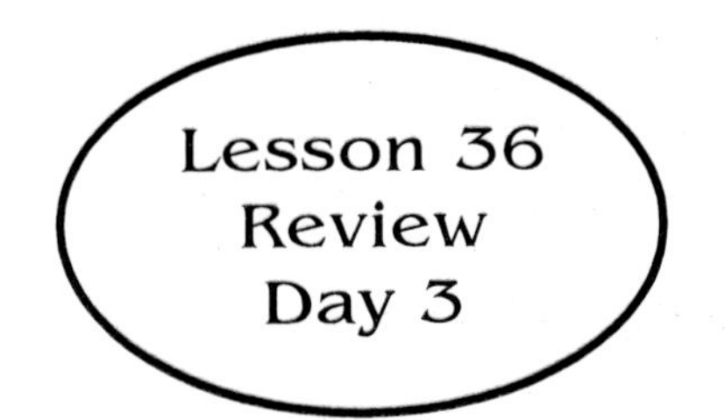

Date: ____________________

Review of Giving Directions

A. Can you tell what is wrong with the following two sets of **directions**? Underline the correct answer in each group.

1. -First, start at the intersection of Pine and Main Street. Travel south.

   -Then, when you see the red barn, travel east.

   -Next, turn on 3rd Street.

   -Finally, turn right on Bacon Street.

   a. The directions do not say where to start.

   b. The directions do not tell which way to turn on 3rd Street.

   c. The directions are out of order.

   d. The directions do not tell which direction to travel once you see the red barn.

2. -First, start at the intersection of South Street and Pine Drive. Drive south on South Street until you see the water tower; turn left.

   -Next, travel for one mile on Post Road.

   -Then, at the intersection of Post road and Giles Ave., travel for five miles.

   -Finally, when you see the green car, turn left and travel on Bishop Court for three miles until you reach your destination.

   a. The directions use too many landmarks.

   b. The directions do not tell what to do when you come to the intersection of Post Road and Giles Ave.

   c. These directions have too many turns.

   d. There is nothing wrong with these directions.

Date: ______________________

Review of How-to Writing

A. Circle the correct answer for each question.

1. What is the first step to writing a **how-to** story?
   a. creating detail sentences
   b. create a main topic
   c. think of subtopics for your story
   d. make sure the main topic is not too narrow or broad

2. From what are detail sentences created?
   a. main topic
   b. subtopics/details
   c. introductory sentence

3. What is the purpose of an ending sentence?
   a. to summarize an entire multiple paragraph story
   b. to summarize a detail sentence
   c. to take the place of an introductory sentence
   d. to end a paragraph

4. From what do we develop a topic sentence?
   a. detail sentences
   b. main topic
   c. ending sentences
   d. introductory sentence

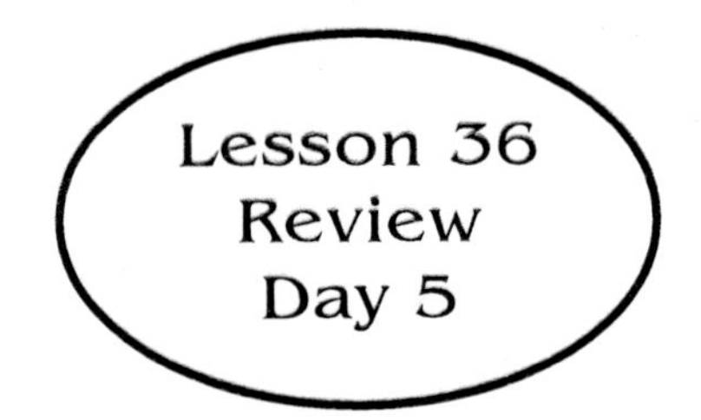

Date: ____________________

Review of How-to Writing

A. Below are two story starters that act as **main topics** for a **how-to** paragraph. These main topics can be used to create **subtopics (steps)** for performing a task. Write three **subtopics (steps)** for each story starter below.

1. how to clean your room

-
-
-

2. how to brush your teeth

-
-
-

Appendix A

Outlining Process for a Single Paragraph

The **writing process** actually has two parts, the **outlining process** and the **drafting process**. The outlining process is the **act of gathering information** necessary to complete a **rough outline** and a **final outline**. This appendix will explain only the outlining process. The drafting process will be covered in each individual lesson where it is needed.

As mentioned above, there are two items that need to be completed during the outlining process, the rough outline and the final outline.

Complete the rough outline

The outlining process starts by completing the rough outline. After the rough outline is complete, the information it contains will be used to develop a final outline. The final outline will then be used as a guide to write a rough draft of the paragraph. Below is a sample rough outline that shows its parts.

Rough Outline

- Main Topic
    - Detail #1: (used to make detail sentences
    - Detail #2: on the final outline)
    - Detail #3:

May be more or fewer than three

Step #1 (develop a main topic for the rough outline)

The first piece of information needed to complete the rough outline is a **main topic**. A main topic is a **very general idea** that tells what a paragraph is about. For example, let's assume we have decided that we want to write a paragraph about **arctic animals**. This bolded phrase is called the **main topic** of the paragraph. Notice that we called this a phrase and not a sentence. A main topic does not have to be a complete sentence. It only needs to be a very general **idea** for your paragraph.

A. When you decide on a main topic, write it in the **main topic** section of your rough outline.

Step #2 (develop details for the rough outline)

Now that we have a main topic (the sample is **arctic animals)**, we need to think of **details** to complete the rough outline. A detail is a thought, phrase, or sentence that gives more information about the main topic. These details will be turned into **detail sentences** for the **final outline**.

Assume we possess no knowledge of our example main topic arctic animals, so we conducted some research to gather information from the library, Internet, and some other dependable sources. Our research returned the following **details** about arctic animals:

1. polar bears
2. seals
3. orcas

These are **details** because they provide more description to the main topic of **arctic animals**.

B. Think of a few details for your main topic and write them under the **details** portion of the rough outline. With the addition of your **details**, the rough outline is complete.

Complete the final outline

The next step in organizing our paragraph is completing a final outline that has the following structure:

- Topic sentence:
- Detail Sentence #1: (constructed from the main
- Detail Sentence #2: topic and details in the
- Detail Sentence #3: rough outline)
- Ending sentence:
  (restates the topic sentence and/or summarizes the detail sentences)

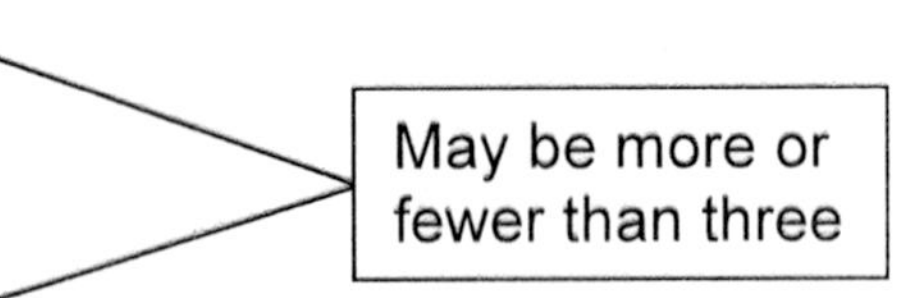

Step #1 (write a topic sentence)

The first step to completing a final outline is writing a **topic sentence**. A topic sentence tells **generally** what the paragraph is about, but it does not provide specific detail about the paragraph. Its primary purpose is to get the attention of the reader.

By looking at the **main topic** and **details** written on the rough outline, we can use them to think of a **topic sentence** for the final outline. While the main topic in the rough outline may or may not be a complete sentence, the topic sentence in the final outline **must** be a complete sentence. Using our example main topic of **arctic animals**, our topic sentence could be something like the following sentence: **Arctic animals survive very well in the extreme cold**.

Step #2 (writing detail sentences)

The next piece of information needed to build the final outline is detail sentences. Detail sentences will make up the greatest portion of your writing. They actually tell the story of the paragraph. This makes the detail sentences arguably the most important part of the writing.

Look at the **details** written on the rough outline. It is our goal to use these **details** along with the **main topic** and **topic sentence** to think of interesting detail sentences for the paragraph. While you are thinking of these **detail sentences**, remember that they will all need to fit together as a paragraph. By the time you are done you should have several detail sentences written under the **detail sentences** section of the final outline. Make sure to place the detail sentences in the correct order if there is a required order for your writing.

Since you now have all of the information you need to think of detail sentences, write your detail sentences in the detail sentences section of the final outline.

After looking at our details, main topic, and topic sentence from our example (arctic animals), we added some detail sentences to our final outline. Our final outline now looks like this:

<u>Final Outline</u>

Topic Sentence:

Arctic animals survive very well in the extreme cold.

Detail Sentences:

- Polar bears have a thick, furry coat which acts as a barrier to the cold.
- Seals have a thick layer of blubber and skin that protects them from the cold.
- Orcas can survive in cold water because they have a thick layer of blubber over their body.

Ending Sentence:

(not developed yet)

Step #3 (writing an ending sentence)

The last step to completing the final outline is to create an **ending sentence**. It is the function of the ending sentence to restate the topic sentence or summarize the detail sentences. For our example above, we could write the following ending sentence:

> "As you can see, most arctic animals that survive the cold have blubber or some kind of insulation."

Create an ending sentence for your paragraph and write it on the **ending sentence** section of your final outline. With the addition of the ending sentence, your final outline is complete.

Appendix B

Outlining Process for Multiple Paragraphs

The **writing process** actually has two parts, the **outlining process** and the **drafting process**. The outlining process is the **act of gathering information** necessary to complete a **rough outline** and a **final outline**. This appendix will explain only the outlining process. The drafting process will be covered in each individual lesson where it is needed.

As mentioned above, there are two items that need to be completed during the outlining process, the rough outline and the final outline.

You will notice that the outlining process for writings with multiple paragraphs is a bit different than the outlining process for a single paragraph. Here are the differences between the two:

1. When multiple paragraphs are required in a writing, they are essentially grouped together to form a larger story or writing. When we have a single paragraph, the reader relies on its topic sentence to tell what the following paragraph is about. In comparison, when multiple paragraphs are grouped together, there is no such sentence or paragraph present that introduces the **entire** writing. Each individual paragraph has its own topic sentence, but none of the topic sentences introduce **all** of the paragraphs. Therefore, when multiple paragraphs are present there needs to be a separate paragraph to introduce or explain **all** of the paragraphs that will be in the writing. This paragraph is called an **introductory paragraph**.
2. The same can be said for a paragraph that concludes the entire writing. Each individual paragraph has an ending sentence, but there is no sentence or paragraph that summarizes the **entire** writing. Therefore, when multiple paragraphs are present there needs to be a separate paragraph to conclude the entire writing. This paragraph is called the **concluding paragraph**.
3. Since many paragraphs are being grouped together, the writer needs a way to identify each paragraph within the writing. The way this is accomplished is by numbering each

paragraph as a subtopic. If you look closely at the rough outline or the final outline of a writing with multiple paragraphs, you will see that a subtopic is simply the same thing as a main topic. Of course each subtopic represents a separate paragraph within the writing. As you can see, each numbered subtopic still contains a topic sentence, detail sentences, and an ending sentence.

- - - - -

We will now start the task of completing the outlining process.

<u>Complete the rough outline</u>

The outlining process starts by completing the rough outline. After the rough outline is complete, the information it contains will be used to develop a final outline. The final outline will then be used as a guide to write a rough draft of the multi-paragraph story/writing.

Step #1 (develop a main topic for the rough outline)

The first piece of information needed to complete the rough outline is a **main topic**. A main topic is a **very general idea** that tells what the story is about. For example, let's assume we have decided that we want to write a story about **arctic animals**. This bolded phrase is called the **main topic** of the story. Notice that we called this a phrase and not a sentence? A main topic does not have to be a sentence. A main topic is a very general **idea** for your writing.

A. When you decide on a main topic for your writing, write it in the **main topic** section of your rough outline for the appropriate lesson. On the next page is a sample rough outline for stories/writings with multiple paragraphs.

Rough Outline

- Main Topic

- Subtopic #1:
- Detail #1: (used to make detail
- Detail #2: sentences on the final
- Detail #3: outline)

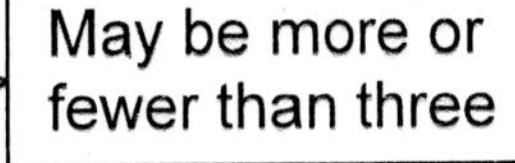

- Subtopic #2:
- Detail #1:
- Detail #2:
- Detail #3:

- Subtopic #3:
- Detail #1:
- Detail #2:
- Detail #3:

Step #2 (developing subtopics for the rough outline)

Your writing will be comprised of one **introductory paragraph**, two or more paragraphs that form the middle part or **body**, and one **concluding paragraph**. This means that you will have to separate your writing into three pieces (introductory paragraph, body, and concluding paragraph).

Since the **body** of your writing will be made up of more than one paragraph, you must develop a **subtopic** (main topic) for each paragraph. Of course this means that each **subtopic** will represent a paragraph in your writing. For our sample story, we have selected three subtopics (your assignment may have more or fewer subtopics) which means that there will be three paragraphs that form the body of our writing.

After adding a **main topic** and **subtopics**, here is how the rough outline for our sample story looks so far:

Main Topic: arctic animals
Subtopic #1: polar bears
    Details: (not yet developed)
Subtopic #2: seals
    Details: (not yet developed)
Subtopic #3: orcas
    Details: (not yet developed)

A. Write the required number of subtopics on the rough outline for your writing. Make sure you write them in the correct order when they occur in your story (if a correct order is necessary).

Step #3 (developing **details** for the rough outline)

Now that you have developed a main topic and your subtopics, you will next need to develop **details** to complete the rough outline. A detail can be a thought, phrase, or sentence that gives more information about the subtopic. These details will later be turned into **detail sentences** for the **final outline**.

Assume that we possess no knowledge of our example main topic arctic animals. With this in mind, we conducted some research to gather information from the library, Internet, and some other dependable sources.

For our sample writing we came up with the following **details** for each subtopic:

Main Topic: arctic animals

Subtopic #1: polar bears
Detail #1: **white fur**
Detail #2: **blubber**
Detail #3: **powerful**

Subtopic #2: seals
Detail #1: **fur**
Detail #2: **thick blubber**
Detail #3: **fast swimmer**

Subtopic #3: orcas
Detail #1: **blubber**
Detail #2: **fast swimmer**
Detail #3: **top of food chain**

Our rough outline is now complete. You can see that by adding details to the rough outline the story is starting to become clearer.

B. Think of a few details for each subtopic in your writing and add them under the appropriate **detail** sections of your rough outline. With the addition of your **details**, your rough outline is complete.

Complete the final outline

You will notice that the rough outline and the final outline **both** have numbered **subtopics** (subtopic #1, subtopic #2, and subtopic #3 in our example) and **details**. The information contained in subtopic #1 in the rough outline (including the details) is used to build subtopic #1 on the final outline, and so on.

We will now start constructing our final outline which has the following structure:

Final Outline

- Introductory Paragraph: (introduces the entire writing)

- Subtopic #1: (can be as many subtopics as necessary)
  - Topic Sentence: (tells about the paragraph)
  - Detail Sentence #1: (constructed from the main
  - Detail Sentence #2: topic and details in the
  - Detail Sentence #3: rough outline)
  - Ending Sentence: (restates the topic sentence or summarizes the detail sentences.)

May be more or fewer than three

- Subtopic #2:
  - Topic Sentence:
  - Detail Sentence #1:
  - Detail Sentence #2:
  - Detail Sentence #3:
  - Ending Sentence:

- Subtopic #3:
  - Topic Sentence:
  - Detail Sentence #1:
  - Detail Sentence #2:
  - Detail Sentence #3:
  - Ending Sentence:

- Concluding Paragraph: (summarizes the entire writing)

Step #1 (writing topic sentences)

The first step to complete the final outline is writing **topic sentences** for each subtopic. A topic sentence (the same thing as a main topic for a single paragraph) tells **generally** what the paragraph that follows is about, but it does not provide specific detail about the writing. Its primary purpose is to get the attention of the reader.

By looking at the **subtopics** and **details** written on the **rough outline**, we can use them to think of **topic sentences** for each **subtopic** in the final outline. While the subtopics on the **rough outline** may not be complete sentences, each **topic sentence** on the final outline must be a complete sentence.

A. For each subtopic on your rough outline, write a **topic sentence** in the appropriate **subtopic** section of the **final outline**.

If you would like to see the subtopic sentences we wrote for our sample writing, go to the end of this appendix.

Step #2 (writing detail sentences)

The next piece of information needed to build the final outline is detail sentences. Detail sentences will make up the greatest portion of your writing. They actually tell the story of the writing (each paragraph). This makes the detail sentences the most important part of the writing.

Look at the **details** written on the rough outline. It is our goal to use these **details**, along with the **topic sentences** you just wrote in the subtopics sections of the final outline, to think of interesting detail sentences for each **subtopic** (paragraph) in the final outline. While you are thinking of these **detail sentences**, remember that they will all need to fit together as a paragraphs. By the time you are done you should have several detail sentences written under the **detail sentences** sections of the final outline. Make sure to place the detail sentences in the correct order for each paragraph if there is a required order for your writing.

B. Since you now have all of the information you need to develop detail sentences, write your detail sentences in the appropriate **detail sentence** sections of the final outline.

Step #3 (write ending sentences)

The next step to complete the final outline is to create an **ending sentence** for each subtopic. It is the function of each ending sentence to restate the subtopic or summarize the detail sentences of that particular paragraph. If you would like to see the ending sentences for our sample, go to the end of this appendix.

C. Write your ending sentences in the appropriate **Ending sentence** sections of the final outline.

Step #4 (write introductory and concluding paragraphs)

The **introductory paragraph** sets the stage for the rest of the writing. This paragraph may introduce characters or provide other information the reader needs to know to understand the writing as a whole. Of course the introductory paragraph may also act to summarize the **subtopics** that follow.

D. Write an introductory paragraph in the **introductory paragraph** section of the final outline.

The last paragraph is the **concluding paragraph**. A concluding paragraph is used to summarize the entire writing. It may also be used to tell the ending of what you are writing.

E. Write a **concluding paragraph** in the concluding paragraph section of the final outline.

Your final outline is now complete! Our final outline for **arctic animals** is on the next page.

Here is our completed final outline:

Final Outline - **Arctic Animals**

- Introductory Paragraph:
  There are many animals that are built to not only endure the extreme cold of the arctic, but also to like this type of weather. We will now discuss three of my favorite arctic animals: the polar bear, seal, and orca.
- Subtopic #1:
  - Topic Sentence:
    Polar bears are large animals that survive in the arctic.
  - Detail Sentence #1:
    Although polar bears have thick white fur, their skin is black.
  - Detail Sentence #2:
    Polar bears are able to survive the extreme cold because they have a thick layer of fat.
  - Detail Sentence #3:
    Polar bears are powerful and fierce land predators in the arctic.
  - Ending Sentence:
    Polar bears are able to survive the extreme cold because their bodies are suited to this weather, and they do not have any enemies.
- Subtopic #2:
  - Topic Sentence:
    Seals are mostly water creatures that can survive extremely cold weather.
  - Detail Sentence #1:
    Although seals look like they have slick skin, they actually have thick fur.
  - Detail Sentence #2:
    Seals also have a thick layer of blubber that allows them to withstand the cold.
  - Detail Sentence #3:
    Seals are very fast swimmers, which enables them to escape from enemies.
  - Ending Sentence:
    Seals are very well suited to survive in the extreme cold, although they do have to watch out for predators.
- Subtopic #3:
  - Topic Sentence:
    Orcas are large water creatures that survive in the arctic.
  - Detail Sentence #1:
    Orcas also have a thick layer of blubber which allows them to survive in cold climates.
  - Detail Sentence #2:
    Orcas are very fast swimmers, which allows them to catch prey.
  - Detail Sentence #3:
    Orcas have very sharp teeth and powerful jaws; this places them at the top of the arctic water food chain.

- o Ending Sentence:
  Orcas are very well suited to survive the cold, and they are the top predator of arctic waters.

- Concluding Paragraph:
  All animals that live in the arctic have adapted to endure such a cold climate. Almost all have some sort of blubber or fat layer that enables them to withstand the cold. For some, enduring the cold is only part of the battle, especially when they are not the top predator.

- - -

Here is how this final outline would look as a written story:

There are many animals that are built to not only endure the extreme cold of the arctic, but also to like this type of weather. We will now discuss three of my favorite arctic animals: the polar bear, seal, and orca.

Polar bears are large animals that survive in the arctic. Although polar bears have thick white fur, their skin is black. Polar bears are able to survive the extreme cold because they have a thick layer of fat. Polar bears are powerful and fierce land predators in the arctic. Polar bears are able to survive the extreme cold because their bodies are suited to this weather, and they do not have any enemies.

Seals are mostly water creatures that can survive extremely cold weather. Although seals look like they have slick skin, they actually have thick fur. Seals also have a thick layer of blubber that allows them to withstand the cold. Seals are also fast swimmers, which enables them to escape from enemies. Seals are very well suited to survive in the extreme cold, although they do have to watch out for predators.

Orcas are large water creatures that survive in the arctic. Orcas also have a thick layer of blubber which allows them to survive in cold climates. Orcas are very fast swimmers, which allows them to catch prey. Orcas have very sharp teeth and powerful jaws; this places them at the top of the arctic water food chain. Orcas are very well suited to survive the cold, and they are the top predator of arctic waters.

All animals that live in the arctic have adapted to endure such a cold climate. Almost all have some sort of blubber or fat layer that enables them to withstand the cold. For some, enduring the cold is only part of the battle, especially when they are not the top predator.

Appendix C

Mark	Use	Example	Final Outcome
	Remove/Omit	kitchhen	kitchen
	Delete space	the k itchen	the kitchen
	Insert	the kithen (c)	the kitchen
	Move as directed	the kitchen hot	the hot kitchen
/	Make lower case	Kitchen	kitchen
	Capitalize	kitchen	Kitchen
¶	New Paragraph	The toy was red and the boy was happy. ¶ He played with it.	The toy was red and the boy was happy. He played with it.
⊙	Insert Punctuation	The kitchen⊙	The kitchen.
[ ]	Center	[kitchen]	kitchen
||←	Move left or right	||← kitchen	kitchen
	Transpose/reverse	kithcen	kitchen
#	Insert space	Thekitchen	The kitchen
||	Align	||The kitchen is hot. The kitchen is red.	The kitchen is hot. The kitchen is red.